Denial Management Counseling

Professional Guide

Denial Management Counseling

Professional Guide

**Advanced Clinical Skills for Motivating
Substance Abusers to Recover**

By Terence T. Gorski
Project Team: Terence T. Gorski,
Stephen F. Grinstead, Arthur B.
Trundy, Joseph E. Troiani, and
Roland F. Williams

Based on the GORSKI-CENAPS®, Model
Better Treatment, for More People, at a Lower Cost

Additional copies are available from the publisher:
  Herald House/Independence Press
  P.O. Box 390
  Independence, MO 64051-0390
  Phone: 1-800-767-8181

For training contact:
  The CENAPS® Corporation®
  17900 Dixie Highway
  Homewood, IL 60430
  Phone: (708) 799-5000

Copyright 2000
Terence T. Gorski
Printed in the United States of America

Library of Congress Cataloging-in-Publication Data

ISBN 0-8309-0965-6

Dedication

This book is dedicated to my children Terence Joseph (TJ) Gorski and Nika Marie Gorski who have added a new depth and richness to my life. I send all of my love to them both now and forever

Table of Contents

Acknowledgments

There are many people and organizations that deserve special acknowledgment for making this professional guide and the workbook possible. First, there is *Stephen F. Grinstead* of CENAPS West who helped me conceptualize and bring the books into final form. Second is *Joseph E. Troiani*, my colleague and lifelong friend, who completed extensive field testing with the Department of the Army and with his addiction classes at the Adler School of Professional Psychology in Chicago, Illinois. Third, there is *Rick Glantz* of Rhea Jacobson Management who both field-tested the materials and helped me find the appropriate title for this book. Fourth is the CENAPS training team who field-tested this course as instructors, including *Steve Grinstead, Roland Williams, Arthur Trundy,* and *Joseph E. Troiani.* Finally, *Tresa Watson* and *Tina Lee*, the staff of the CENAPS Central office in Chicago, Illinois, played a vital role in coordinating innumerable details and behind-the-scenes work that the field testing and publication of these materials required.

The clinical materials on which this book was based were field tested in three-day clinical skills training format twenty-six times by sixteen organizations involving more than 750 experienced addiction and mental health therapists in the development process. Special acknowledgment needs to be given to the members of this nationwide team listed below:

1. Academy of Health Sciences, Department of the Army, Fort Sam Houston, Texas:
   - *Trainer:* Joseph E. Troiani
   - 7 DMC Field Tests: (#1) 5/19–21/98, (#2) 8/11–13/98, (#3) 1/12–14/99, (#4) 3/16–18/99, (#5) 6/8–10/99, (#6) 8/17–19/99, and (#7) 11/15–17/99 all in San Antonio, TX
2. Bridge House, New Orleans, LA:

- *Trainer:* Stephen F. Grinstead
- 1 DMC Field Test: 9/22–24/99 in New Orleans, LA
3. CENAPS West, Cupertino, CA
   - *Trainer:* Stephen F. Grinstead
   - 1 DMC Field Test Date: 8/25–27/99 in San Francisco, CA
4. Ernst Kennedy Center, Charleston, SC
   - *Trainer:* Arthur B. Trundy
   - 2 DMC Field Test: (#1) 8/25–27/99; and (#2) 5/15–17/00
5. Family Counseling Services, Cortland, NY
   - *Trainer:* Arthur B. Trundy
   - 1 DMC Field Test Date: 11/01–03/99
6. Maxey Training School, Detroit, MI
   - *Trainer:* Roland F. Williams
   - 2 DMC Field Test Dates: On (#1) 8/24–26/98, and (#2) 12/7–9/98 in Novi, MI
7. New Sunrise Hospital, San Fidel, NM
   - *Trainer:* Roland F. Williams
   - 1 DMC Field Test Date: 9/21–23/99 in San Fidel, NM
8. Resource Alliance Inc., San Jose, CA
   - *Trainer:* Stephen F. Grinstead
   - 1 DMC Field Test: 9/30–10/2/98 in San Jose, CA
9. Rhea Jacobson Management, Battle Ground, WA
   - *Trainer:* Rick Glantz
   - 4 DMC Field Tests: (#1) 11/2–4/99 in Phoenix, AZ; (#2) 10/18–20/99 in Laurel, MD; (#3) 9/27–29/99 in Columbus, OH, (#4) 4/13–15/99 in Phoenix, AZ.
10. Walden House, Inc., San Francisco, CA
    - *Trainer:* Stephen F. Grinstead
    - 1 DMC Field Test Date: 5/5–7/00 in San Francisco, CA
11. Washington Department of Corrections (WADOC), Airway Heights, WA
    - *Trainer:* Terence T. Gorski
    - 1 DMC Field Test Date: 4/20–22/99 in Spokane, WA
12. Westbrook Health Services, Parkersberg, WV
    - *Trainer:* Arthur B. Trundy
    - 1 DMC Field Test Date: 1/26–28/00 in Parkersberg, WV
13. Alameda City Health Services Agency, Oakland, CA
    - *Trainer:* Roland F. Williams

- 1 DMC Field Test: 7/27/99 in Alameda, CA
14. Alert Driving, Inc., San Jose, CA
    - *Trainer:* Stephen F. Grinstead
    - 1 DMC Field Test Date: 1/15/99 in San Jose, CA
15. Community Treatment Center, Detroit, MI
    - *Trainer:* Roland F. Williams
    - 1 DMC Field Test Date: 10/12/99 in Detroit, MI
16. High Intensity Drug Trafficking Area (HIDTA), Washington, D.C.
    - *Trainer:* Terence T. Gorski

Introduction

In early 1998 I began to develop a professional guide and workbook for managing denial in people with substance-use disorders. My goal was to take the core clinical processes that had proven so effective in both Relapse Prevention Therapy (RPT) and Relapse Prevention Counseling (RPC) and apply them to managing denial. I created the working title Motivational Recovery Counseling (MRC), which would later be renamed Denial Management Counseling (DMC), and set to work. I soon discovered that this developmental process would not be as simple and straightforward as I first thought. I also discovered how much of our work as clinicians is governed by the principle of **unconscious competence.**

We develop unconscious competence when we learn how to do something primarily through role modeling and clinical experience without the benefit of explicit instruction. We intuitively learn, develop, and use many complex interventions that just seem to come to us at key moments in therapy when we need them. The problem is that we're not always consciously aware of what we do when we have these intuitive moments in therapy. Fortunately, there is a method called **clinical modeling** that can help us.

Clinical modeling is done by watching experienced clinicians work with clients or in role-play sessions to determine what they said and did at key moments in the clinical process. I applied this clinical modeling process to the development of Denial Management Counseling (DMC). Much of the work consisted of recording and analyzing role-play sessions during clinical training workshops. I thought this process would be quick and simple, but I was wrong. Let me explain what happened.

Denial Management Counseling (DMC) was based on my earlier work on managing denial patterns. The idea was to update a **Denial Pattern Checklist** that I had used, with good results, in individual therapy, group therapy, and psycho-education sessions. The checklist was used by asking clients to read the denial patterns out loud, identify denial patterns that applied to them, and personalize the denial patterns for use in self-monitoring. This process helped clients understand what denial is, identify their personal denial patterns, and learn how to manage them.

I updated the Denial Pattern Checklist and developed an initial clinical skills training course to teach counselors and therapists how to use it. In field-testing the course, participants reported that the process worked well with some clients, but the overall feedback told me that I missed something. Clinicians reported two major problems when trying to use the process. First, many clients had such strong denial that they refused to work with the Denial Pattern Checklist. Second, because denial is triggered by thinking and talking about substance use and related problems, many clients could easily avoid or intellectualize the information without seeing how it really applied to them.

From this feedback I developed a second version of the course that linked the recognition and management of denial patterns to the use of a brief, structured assessment process. The assessment guided clients through a detailed self-exploration of their alcohol and drug use and its effects on their life. First, clients identified their presenting problem, determined the relationship of each presenting problems to substance use, and explored the consequences of continued use in terms of their ability to resolve each presenting problem. Next, clients were asked to make two commitments: to work on resolving the presenting problems; and to stay abstinent from alcohol and other drugs during the treatment process. Finally, the clients compared the denial patterns on the checklist to how they responded to the presenting problem analysis and treatment contracting process. This allowed them to identify their personal denial patterns and the related thoughts, feelings, urges, and actions they actually used in the session to deny the problem.

By taking a client through this process, the concept of denial shifted, in the client's mind, from a vague intellectual abstraction to a readily identifiable problem that was creating more problems than it solved. Clients could see how denial was triggered automatically when they began to think or talk about the substance use. This motivated many clients to learn more about denial and how to identify and challenge their own denial patterns. They also began to recognize and manage the strong feelings created when denial is activated. Clients then completed a **Brief Life and Addiction History** and an **Addiction Symptom Checklist**. Whenever the clients started to use denial, it was consciously identified and managed before it created serious problems in the session.

This new training format worked well. Feedback was excellent and it appeared the problems were solved. I went into the second phase of field testing, which involved teaching members of The CENAPS® Training Team to instruct the courses. However, additional problems developed in this phase of field testing.

In the initial training sessions I did extensive clinical demonstrations of the denial management process. Students identified the denial patterns they had observed during each role play, and evaluated the strategies the trainer had used to manage them. I quickly became aware, however, of the number of skills that were being transmitted through the unconscious role-modeling process. In the second version of the course, I was bringing more of my own unconscious competence to the training than I realized. Many of the vital principles and practices were not clearly articulated. They were being transmitted primarily through role modeling during clinical demonstrations and the interactions of the participants during the experiential portions of the training.

As I reflected on this new information, it became apparent that competent clinicians have very different styles in dealing with clients who are using strong denial. I put my skills of clinical modeling to work and developed an explicit series of interactional skills managing denial, which I called **The Denial Management Interactional Process.**

The development of the Denial Management Interactional Process added new information about managing denial that was not available in the original exercises in *The Denial Management Workbook.* So I went to work updating these exercises. I also reviewed the project notes that documented this developmental process. These contained useful information I wanted to make available to other clinicians, so I began writing a *Professional Guide to Denial Management.* As always happens, the work on the professional guide showed gaps and flaws in the workbook, and correcting the workbook exercises showed weaknesses in the professional guide. I recorded the courses I taught, listened to the tapes, and discussed progress and problems with trainers who were teaching the course. As a result, I found more material for the professional guide that spontaneously emerged during the training.

In all things, however, there comes a time when a work in progress must be deemed ready for publication. That time has come and two new products are now ready for release: (1) *Denial Management Counseling Professional Guide: Advanced Clinical Skills for Motivating Substance Abusers to Recover,* and (2) *The Denial Management Counseling Workbook: Practical Exercises for Motivating People with Substance Use Problems to Recovery.* Two separate skills training workshops, a one-day and three-day version, are also available in many cities around the country. An optional competency certification leading to a credential of **Certified Denial Management Specialist** is available for clinicians completing the three-day course and completing a competency certification portfolio.

Thanks for your patience. I hope the quality and depth of these materials will prove to be worth the wait.

Terence T. Gorski
August 2000

Part 1

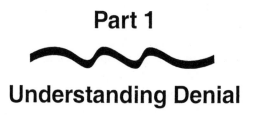

Understanding Denial

1–1. Learning the Denial Management System

Denial is a serious problem that can cause relapse. Most counselors and therapists routinely deal with clients who have severe denial and treatment resistance. Some of these clients have been forced into treatment as a result of serious life problems. Others have been arrested for legal problems such as driving under the influence of alcohol or drugs, or for committing drug-related crimes such as possession or sales of illegal control substances. Still others have been referred by doctors or hospitals because of alcohol or drug-related medical or psychiatric problems or have been forced into treatment due to the threat of job loss, divorce, or loss of the custody of children. Some of these clients are in the early stages of recognizing and managing serious life problems. Others have severe substance use, mental, or personality disorders that lock them into rigid and, at times, unmanageable denial.

These clients are the most difficult to work with because they are masters at denying the relationship of alcohol and drug use to their presenting problems and focusing instead on interesting but irrelevant secondary issues. They are also skilled at getting treatment providers to become part of their alcohol and drug problem by focusing on these secondary problems instead of dealing with the alcohol and drug use that caused or complicated these secondary problems.

Denial Management Counseling (DMC) can help therapists succeed with clients who are locked into patterns of severe denial and treatment resistance. This book will show you how to integrate this denial management system into your personal clinical style. It will also show you how to integrate the system into your clinical practice or treatment program. This book will help you review and organize the skills that you already have for managing denial. It will also help you learn new and powerful denial management skills.

This book is titled *Denial Management Counseling: Advanced Clinical Skills for Motivating Substance Abusers to Recover.* It discusses a number of issues related to motivating clients to recover by using a systematic process to manage denial, overcome treatment resistance, identify serious problems, and motivate your clients to solve them.

The denial management process involves identifying both the **positive personal** and **lifestyle preferences** that will motivate a client toward new behavior and the **self-reinforcing cycles of denial and resistance** that become activated when they began to think or talk about the problems that are preventing them from achieving their goals.

This book will systematically guide you through a series of tools that can be used to effectively manage denial. First, we will review the need for a denial management system, define denial, explain its dynamics, and identify the common denial patterns used by clients in treatment. We will explore the levels of denial by explaining how denial is related to a lack of information, conscious defensiveness, unconscious defense mechanisms, and delusions.

We will then explain denial as a normal and natural human response to severe pain and overwhelming problems. This will lead into a discussion of the basic principles of denial management, which tell us that denial is a normal and natural psychological defense that has both benefits and disadvantages. The biggest disadvantage of denial is that it blocks recognition and problem solving. We will present the two antidotes for denial—acceptance and problem solving—and show that clients can learn to recognize and manage their denial so they can recognize, accept, and learn to solve their problems.

Then we will explore the common denial patterns used by clients who enter counseling and therapy. We will look at both the **Big Five Denial Patterns** (Avoidance, Absolute Denial, Minimizing, Rationalizing, and Blaming) and the **Small Seven Denial Patterns** (Comparing, Manipulating, Recovery by Fear,

Compliance, Flight into Health, Strategic Hopelessness, and the Democratic Disease State). We will show you how these individual denial patterns work together to form a denial strategy.

> ## Denial Management Counseling (DMC)
> 1. The DMC Interactional Process
> 2. The DMC Clinical Exercises
> 3. The DMC Psychoeducational Program

This will lead into an exploration of the denial management process. First, we will explore the goals of the denial management process and the role of confrontation. This will lead us into a description of the three related systems for Denial Management Counseling (DMC): The DMC Interactional Process; the DMC Clinical Exercises; and the DMC Psychoeducational Program

The DMC Interactional Process is a strategy for therapeutic communication that can be used when talking with clients who are exhibiting strong denial and treatment resistance. **The DMC Clinical Exercises** are a series of structured tasks that can be used as the basis of a standard treatment plan for use in individual or problem-solving group therapy. This sequence of exercises teaches clients how to understand, identify, and manage their own denial. **The DMC Psychoeducational Program** (also called Denial Self-Management Training) is a standardized education program for denial management that can be taught classroom style to clients who are having trouble recognizing and managing their denial. When taken together, these three DMC systems provide a structure for building a comprehensive approach to managing denial and resistance that can be used by individual clinicians or as the foundation of a comprehensive denial management program.

Understanding the Denial Management Model
To effectively use the Denial Management System you will need to apply it on four levels. First, you must *understand it.*

This means learning the basic principles and practices. Second, you will need to *integrate it into your personal clinical style.* This means using and taking ownership of the system by customizing it to fit with your current clinical preferences and skills. Third, you will need to *adapt it to the needs of your treatment program.* Finally, you will need to *individualize it to meet the needs of each client.* Let's look at each of these in more detail.

Learning to Use
The Denial Management System

1. Understand the Model
   - *Know the principles and practices*

2. Integrate It into Your Personal Style
   - *Make it an habitual part of your routine practice*

3. Adapt It to the Needs of Your Program
   - *Improve program quality and effectiveness*

4. Individualize It for Each Client
   - *Make a difference in the lives of your clients*

The first goal is to understand the basic principles and practices of Denial Management Counseling (DMC). A *principle* is a fundamental truth or general law on which something is based. DMC is based on the principles of human motivation and psychological defense mechanisms. By the time you finish reading this book you will understand those basic principles.

A *practice* is a behavior or set of behaviors that put a principle into effect. A practice is what we do to turn a principle into a tool for getting things done in the real world. In this book you will learn a set of specific practices designed to identify and effectively manage denial and treatment resistance.

To use DMC effectively you must understand the fundamental principles on which it is based. This is especially true if you want to integrate DMC into your personal clinical style, adapt the practices to the needs and culture of your treatment program, and individualize it to the needs of individual clients.

Integrating Denial Management into Your Personal Style

The second goal is to integrate DMC into your personal clinical style by comparing its principles and practices with your current way of dealing with denial and treatment resistance. In other words, you will need to personalize or take ownership of the system so that you can use it comfortably. This means consciously using the system until it becomes habitual.

Adapting Denial Management to the Needs of Your Program

Ultimately we all will have to take DMC principles and practices back to the real world of clinical practice. There are many different kinds of programs working with many different kinds of clients. To make DMC work you will have to adapt it to meet the needs of your program. You will need to "translate" the system so that you can comfortably integrate it with the clinical culture of your program and adapt the various DMC procedures to fit into the context of existing assessment, psychoeducation, group therapy, and individual therapy programs.

Individualizing Denial Management for Each Client

The real test, however, will come when you begin working face-to-face with individual clients exhibiting denial and resistance. These clients will invite you to become part of their problem. Your old habitual ways of coping with denial and resistance will get activated and it will take a concerted effort for you to use your new skills to stop denial and keep your clients focused on their core issues.

In order to accomplish these four goals, let's start at the beginning and look at an operational definition of denial.

1–2. The Definition of Denial

Before we can learn how to effectively manage denial, we must have a clear understanding of what denial is. Unfortunately, the term denial is often used in such a general manner that it has become a "garbage can diagnostic label." This means that if you can't figure out what is going wrong with your patients, you can diagnose them as being in denial. This is why DMC is based on a clear, concrete, and specific definition of denial that allows us to recognize it when it occurs, differentiate it from other problems or disorders, and design specific and effective interventions for dealing with it.

Here is a general definition of denial: *Denial is the natural tendency to avoid the pain caused by recognizing the presence, severity, and responsibility for dealing with serious problems.*

General Definition of Denial

The natural tendency to avoid the pain caused by recognizing the presence, severity, and responsibility for dealing with serious problems.

This definition tells us that denial is focused on blocking our recognition of three basic facts: first, that we have a problem; second, that the problem is serious; and third, that we are responsible for dealing with it.

We all have a natural tendency to use denial to defend ourselves against the pain caused by overwhelming problems. Whenever we are forced to recognize a painful or overwhelming problem, our minds will activate a defensive program that protects us from the need to think or talk about the problem. When we refuse to think or talk about the problem, the pain temporarily goes away. Unfortunately, so does our ability to recognize and deal effectively with the problem.

Although this general definition of denial is helpful, it is not detailed enough to guide us in developing clinical interventions for denial. Let's look at another definition, an operational definition, that explains the psychological processes used in the denial process. *Denial is a set of automatic and unconscious thoughts, feelings, urges, actions, and social reactions that defend against the pain of recognizing the presence, se-*

verity, and responsibility for dealing with serious problems.
Let's break that definition apart and see what it really means.

Operational Definition of Denial

Denial is a set of automatic and unconscious....

T = Thoughts

F = Feelings

U = Urges

A = Actions

R = Social Reactions

that defend against the pain of recognizing
the presence, severity, and responsibility
for dealing with serious problems.

Denial Is a Set of Reactions

When denial is activated, people react in a way that changes the functioning of their five basic psychosocial systems. These five systems are the cognitive or thinking system, the affective or feeling system, the motivational or urge system, the behavioral action system, and the social or interpersonal system.

This means that we must answer five key or critical questions if we want to thoroughly understand how denial is affecting our clients These questions are:

1. What ways of thinking are preventing clients from seeing the seriousness of their problems?
2. What feelings are preventing them from seeing the seriousness of their problems?
3. What motivations or urges are preventing them from seeing the seriousness of their problems?
4. What actions or behaviors are preventing them from seeing the seriousness of their problems?
5. What social interactions or relationships are preventing them from seeing the seriousness of their problems?

By working with our clients to answer these questions, we

can focus on the specific things our clients are doing that keep them from recognizing the presence, severity, and responsibility for solving their problems. Once we identify exactly what our clients are doing, we can develop strategies to help them become aware of their problems and develop new ways of thinking about the problem, new ways for managing the feelings and urges that are created by the problem, and new ways for dealing with or solving the problem. There is one major problem, however.

> Denial is a set of
> automatic and unconscious reactions
> that are activated when people are asked
> to think about or talk about
> painful or overwhelming problems

Denial is a set of *automatic and unconscious reactions* that are activated when people are asked to think about or talk about painful or overwhelming problems. In other words, the reaction we call denial suddenly happens without the client planning or thinking about it and at times when the therapist doesn't expect it. A trigger goes off and the automatic reactions called denial get turned on.

Most clients are not fully aware of exactly what they are thinking, feeling, or doing when they are in denial. As a result, one of the first steps in managing denial is to help our clients become aware of exactly what triggers activate their denial and what they start thinking, feeling, and doing when the denial is activated. By finding the triggers that activate the denial, we can usually find the problems that our clients are trying to deny.

When the trigger goes off, a set of *automatic thoughts* is turned on. I often describe these thoughts as a tape, because once they are turned on they tend to run through our minds like a message in a tape recorder. Every time we turn on the tape recorder, it starts playing the same message over and over again. Denial, however, is not a single tape-recorded message. It is a collection of related messages that automatically run through our minds when denial is triggered. Each of these tape-recorded messages of denial is to some degree separate and independent of the others, yet they are all inter-related. One tape will make it easier for the next tape to get turned on. As you will see later, there are twelve basic tape-recorded messages of denial, which we call denial patterns.

Once the trigger for denial is activated, the first tape-recorded denial pattern runs through our mind. Often this tape triggers the activation of a second tape, which in turn activates the playing of a third tape and so on. The end result is that most people in denial get trapped in automatic and uncontrollable ways of thinking that get their mind spinning in what feels like an out-of-control pattern. One client told me he felt "possessed by his denial" because it seemed to take on a life of its own and take over his mind.

So people in denial get locked into circular and self-defeating ways of thinking that prevent them from figuring out what is really going on and developing a plan to make things better. Let's look at an example:

John was 32 years old, married with two children, a twelve-year-old daughter and a fourteen-year-old son. John is a responsible person who is a manager in a large warehouse. He was arrested for driving under the influence of alcohol after a dinner meeting with fellow managers in a restaurant that served alcohol. John knew he had been drinking, but he honestly felt he was sober enough to drive safely. He was stopped at a sobriety checkpoint. The officer smelled alcohol on his breath and gave him a roadside test, which he passed. The smell of alcohol was so strong, however, that the officer insisted that John take a breath test. The breath test showed that John had a 0.14 blood alcohol level when the legal limit in his state is 0.1.

As part of the legal process John was referred to an alcohol and drug abuse program for an evaluation. He was angry and scared. He was angry because he believed he was driving safely and was not too drunk to drive. After all, he passed the roadside test. He was scared because he knew he could lose his driver's license and he needed his car to get to work. He was also angry because getting the DUI caused serious conflicts with his wife.

The legal and related fees would cost in the neighborhood of $3,000 and they had better things they could spend that kind of money on. He was also afraid his boss would find out and fire him. He was in a safety-sensitive position supervising people using forklifts and other potentially dangerous machinery. His place of business had zero tolerance for alcohol or drug abuse.

Every time John would start to think about or talk about his DUI with his friends, a trigger would go off in his head and a set of tapes would start to play. They would go something like this:

"I know I shouldn't have been driving after drinking, but the whole thing is so unfair. I passed the roadside test, so how could I have been too drunk to drive? But those cops don't care. They must get bonuses for each person they arrest. Even so, I wasn't that much over the limit. They should have given me a break. What right did they have to take me to jail and force me to post bond? My wife is mad at me and it's not my fault. Now I need to go see a counselor who probably already believes I'm a drunk. I have no choice but to go along because I need my driver's license to get to work. But I know I didn't really do anything wrong. Maybe I shouldn't have been drinking, but what difference does it make? The process is so unfair. There's no way I can win!"

And then the cycle of repetitive tapes would start to play again. Can you guess what John's therapist is going to hear when he or she asks: *"Could you tell me about the problems that caused you to come into counseling at this time?"*

Denial, however, is more than just a set of thoughts. It is also a set of automatic and powerful feelings and emotions that drive the thinking process. As a matter of fact, the thinking process is often out of control because the feelings that drive it are so intense and the thoughts are designed to keep the feelings under control by turning them off. The best way to turn off feelings is not to think or talk about the things that turn them on.

The primary emotional drivers of denial are pain, anger, fear, guilt, and shame. We'll talk more about these later. For now, just remember that when the trigger of denial goes off, powerful automatic feelings and emotions will be activated. There will then be a dynamic interplay between the automatic thoughts and the automatic feelings.

The Primary Emotional Drivers of Denial

1. Pain
2. Anger
3. Fear
4. Guilt
5. Shame

The goal of the denial-related thoughts is to manage the overwhelming feelings. The denial-related thoughts temporally relieve these feelings in the short run, but in the long run the denial will intensify the feelings that were initially turned off. When these intensified feelings return, they will drive the person to use more denial-related thinking, with more conviction, until the thoughts become deeply believed and habituated. This process of using denial-related thoughts to manage the feelings caused by a problem occurs repeatedly, until finally the use of denial becomes an automatic and unconscious habit. Because this vicious cycle of the denial process intensifies the feelings, the process can easily spiral out of control.

The thoughts and feelings that are part of the denial process activate strong *automatic urges to act out* by using resistant and self-defeating behavior. The overall goal of denial is to avoid pain by either blocking out or distorting information about the problem that is causing the pain or by doing something else that creates a distraction.

It is much easier to channel energy into fighting an enemy than it is to face an unsolvable catastrophic problem that is creating overwhelming pain, anger, fear, guilt. and shame. The urge is usually to act out against someone else by turning them into an enemy. Because the therapist is often the only person in the direct line of fire, guess who usually gets invited to become the enemy?

So remember, clients in denial are sitting in front of you trying to control a set of self-destructive urges. They may have become masters at hiding these urges and the feelings that are driving them, but don't be fooled. Clients in denial can be easily triggered into an emotional overreaction marked by out-of-control behavior.

Denial is also a set of automatic and unconscious behaviors. These behaviors are by their very nature self-defeating because they are used to avoid, minimize, or distort knowledge about the problems and either block out or redirect feelings toward someone or something else. The person using these behaviors, however, feels backed into a corner. At the moment when the denial is activated, they see no other choice except to use these resistant behaviors to try and get out of the trap that was created by the people forcing them to think and talk about the problem that is causing them so much pain.

Denial Causes Social Reactions

Denial and resistant behaviors can trigger a relatively predictable set of social reactions in people who try to help. Only one thing is certain. If you allow yourself to use socially appropriate responses that most "normal people" would use to respond to irrational denial and resistance, you are bound to become part of the problem instead of part of the solution. It is important to control your tendency to react to your clients without thinking. Hold back, observe, and let your clinical reasoning control your tendency to react emotionally.

My grandfather, who was a farmer, once told me, *"Never get into a pissing contest with a skunk, the skunk will win every time."* People in denial want you to confront them harshly. They know how to deal with that. They know how to take your direct confrontation and turn it back against you. They know how to use your confrontation to prove they are right and you are wrong. And most importantly, they know how to use your confrontations to manipulate you into becoming part of their problem instead of part of their solution.

Denial Defends Against the Pain of Recognizing Serious Problems

People use denial because they are hurting so bad they don't know what else to do. This is the most important thing that every therapist needs to understand. People use denial because, at that moment, they are hurting really bad and they don't know what else to do. **Denial is the last refuge of the**

incompetent. We tend to use denial when we don't know what else we can do to manage the pain. Most of the time we are not even consciously aware we are doing it.

> People use denial because
> they are hurting so bad
> they don't know what else to do.

Denial is an automatic and unconscious reaction. *Automatic* means that we do it spontaneously in response to a stimulus or trigger. *Unconscious* means that we do it without thinking. We start acting out to defend ourselves before we have time to think it through. If we try to think it through, we find these powerful thoughts that are difficult to control running through our heads and we don't know how to turn them off.

Denial management counseling can give us a set of principles for understanding denial and a set of clinical practices (clinical tools) that are effective in teaching your clients to recognize and manage their tendency to lapse into denial.

The only effective way to manage denial is to teach your clients self-management strategies. If you try to force your clients out of their denial, you will probably just strengthen it. Remember my grandfather's advise: *"Don't get into a pissing contest with a skunk! The skunk will win every time."* Apply that wisdom to dealing with clients in denial. Don't get into a power struggle with someone who is an expert at denial and resistance. The solution is to learn the gentle art of sneaking up from behind. That is what Denial Management Counseling (DMC) is all about: learning how to use supportive and directive methods to teach clients what denial is, get them to see the denial patterns they are using to avoid facing their problems, and then teaching them methods to turn off the denial so they can identify, clarify, and resolve the painful problems causing the denial.

Before discussing how to teach clients to recognize and manage denial, I want to discuss the different levels at which denial can operate.

> The only effective way to manage denial
> is to teach your clients
> denial self-management strategies.

1–3. The Levels of Denial

Denial operates at different levels of severity or intensity. Many people mistakenly believe that denial operates like a light switch with two positions—on and off. The light is either on and you're in denial, or it's off and you're not in denial. In reality, denial operates more like a variable intensity light switch that allows you to tune in various levels of brightness. Denial can take the form of a lack of information, a conscious defensiveness, an unconscious defensiveness, or a full-blown delusion. Let's look at each of these levels of denial in more detail.

Levels of Denial

1. **Lack of Information**
   • Wrong information about addiction and recovery

2. **Conscious Defensiveness**
   • Knowledge that something is wrong but refusal to face the pain of knowing

3. **Unconscious Defensiveness**
   • Automatic evasion and distortion that guards against severe pain and helplessness

4. **Delusion**
   • Deeply entrenched mistaken beliefs held despite overwhelming evidence that they are not true

---

Level 1. Denial as a Lack of Information

Many times we say a person is "in denial" when they simply lack accurate information about what is wrong with them.

I once asked a client, *"Do you believe you are an alcoholic?"* He answered with an emphatic no. Yet I could see from looking at his records that he was referred for his second charge of driving under the influence of alcohol (DUI) and admitted to having some problems with his wife and his boss regarding his heavy drinking. Was this client in denial?

I wasn't sure so I asked another question: *"What is your definition of an alcoholic?"* The client answered immediately: *"An alcoholic is a skid-row bum who doesn't work, has no family, and is totally irresponsible."*

Then I asked, *"Why don't you think you're an alcoholic?"* The client said, *"Because I have a job. I work hard every day. I have a family and I take good care of them. I'm not like those irresponsible good-for-nothing drunks."*

This client did not have accurate information about alcoholism. I discussed what alcoholism was, explained the common misperceptions, including the mistaken belief that all alcoholics are skid-row bums. I then explained the symptoms and guided him through a self-assessment process. He was able to see that he had a problem with drinking and that his drinking problem was, in fact, a serious disease or medical condition called alcoholism.

As we explored his social history he told me his father had died of cirrhosis of the liver that was caused by heavy drinking. My client never considered his father an alcoholic because his father had held down a job and provided for his family. His father had died under the care of the best doctors in a first-class hospital paid for by private insurance. The client told me that after learning what alcoholism really is, he had to think again about his conclusion that his father was not alcoholic.

Was this client in denial? No. This client lacked accurate information about alcoholism and addiction. Once he received that information, he was able to face the truth without having to use denial to defend himself against the pain of knowing.

It is a good idea to assume that clients who appear to be in denial are lacking accurate information about what addiction is. If they are truly in denial, when you try to give them accurate information, denial patterns will get activated that will prevent them from understanding or accepting what you are trying to explain.

Level 2. Denial as a Conscious Defensiveness

Many clients don't respond well to accurate information about their addiction. I worked with another client who was referred as a result of his second arrest for driving under the influence of alcohol (DUI). He also denied being an alcoholic and had serious misinformation about what alcoholism was. When I gave accurate information about alcohol abuse and alcoholism his response was, *"So what's that got to do with me? Are you calling me a drunk?"*

This client was definitely defensive. It turned out he was consciously defending himself from having to think or talk about his drinking. I discovered this when I asked him, *"Is there a part of you that thinks you might have a problem with alcohol or drugs?"*

He said, *"Sure, doesn't everyone?"* Then he told me about how, from time to time, he thinks he might drink too much and would be better off if he cut back. He ended by saying, *"But I'm sure it's nothing serious. If I wouldn't have hit that sobriety checkpoint everything would be fine!"*

This client experienced denial as a conscious or semiconscious defensiveness. He had an inner conflict about whether he had a drinking problem or not. Part of him said he did. Another part of him said he didn't. He was aware of both parts of this inner dialogue. The strongest inner voice was the part of him that said he was not alcoholic, but he was aware and able to talk about the part of him that had some doubts.

When I asked him if we could look at both sides of the argument, he agreed. We did a structured inner dialogue between the part of him that believed he was fine despite his alcohol-related problems (I called this the Addictive Self) and the part of him that thought he might have a problem and would be better off if he quit drinking (I called this the Sober Self). Because he was aware of the inner conflict, the work was very productive and he could see the irrationality behind his thinking. He then agreed to go through an addiction evaluation while carefully self-monitoring for the inner voice that tried to persuade him not to think or talk about his drinking, drugging, and related problems. Once this client consciously recognized his inner conflict, he was able to understand and apply the information about addiction that he previously felt did not apply to him.

Level 3. Denial as an Unconscious Defense Mechanism

Some clients practice denial for such a long time that they start using it without having to think about it. A psychologist would say the denial has become an unconsciously integrated part of their personality.

An easier way to understand this is to think about the inner dialogue that goes on in the head of people who are consciously defensive about their drinking problem. One part of them says, "*Yes, I have a problem. I need to do something about it.*" Another part of them says, *"No, I don't have a problem. Everything is fine. There's no need to change."*

Now suppose that this argument were going on in their head week after week, month after month, and year after year. Suppose further that every time they had this argument, the addictive voice that said, *"You don't have a problem!"* won out over the sober voice that said, *"You do have a problem!"*

Eventually they would accept the position of the Addictive Self that said, "*I don't have a problem*" as being true. Once they accept the addictive voice as true, they stop fighting with themselves because they know the right answer. They get in the habit of letting the Addictive Self win by defeating the Sober Self. So whenever the argument starts in their heads, it ends quickly and they don't even notice that they had an inner conflict. The only part of the argument they are aware of is the Addictive Self that says, *"You don't have a problem and anyone who thinks that you do is crazy!"*

Once this happens, denial becomes an unconscious defense mechanism that takes on a life of its own. Because clients experiencing this level of denial are not aware they are in a conflict, it is more difficult to work with them. *This is the level of denial that responds best to the DMC Interactional Process.*

DMC uses active listening to expose the denial and then explains to clients the form of denial they are using. DMC allows clients to see what they are doing, to understand it, and to become consciously aware of the inner conflict and the underlying pain from using denial to protect themselves. Once they become aware of the inner conflict, they move into conscious defensiveness and the techniques described earlier are effective.

Many years ago a Native American counselor asked me this question: *"If you had two fighting dogs of the same size and breed, a red dog and blue dog, and you put them in a pit to fight each other, which dog would win?"* When I said I didn't know, he answered, *"The dog you fed and trained the most."*

When clients are using denial as an unconscious and automatic habit, you can be sure they have been feeding and training the red dog of addiction while starving the blue dog of sobriety. As a result, the Addictive Self takes over and the client stops using sober and responsible thinking.

Question:	"If you had two fighting dogs of the same size and breed, a red dog and blue dog, and you put them in a pit to fight each other, which dog would win."
Answer:	"The dog you fed and trained the most."

Level 4. Denial as a Delusion

Sometimes clients become committed to believing that nothing is wrong when it really is. They rehearse this belief in their own mind until it becomes nearly unshakable. At that point, the denial has progressed to something more severe than an unconscious defense mechanism. It has become a delusion. For some people this deeply entrenched delusional denial may be part of a related personality or mental disorder. But just what is a delusion?

A delusion is a mistaken belief that is firmly held despite convincing evidence that it is not true.

A delusion is a mistaken belief that is firmly held despite convincing evidence that it is not true. When people are delusional they will adjust other perceptions and beliefs in order to prove that the delusion is true.

A psychiatrist once treated a patient with an interesting delusion: The patient believed he was dead. The doctor could only find one small crack in this patient's delusional system. The patient firmly believed that "dead men don't bleed!" To break the delusion the doctor took the man's finger, pricked it with a needle, and squeezed out a large drop of blood. As the man looked at his own bleeding finger, he became white as a ghost. He started to tremble and said, *"My God, dead men do bleed!"*

In most clients, firmly held delusions result from the cognitive impairment that goes along with having coexisting disorders that share the same defensive structures. In such cases it is important to recognize that denial is best managed in the context of dual disorder treatment.

Summarizing the Levels of Denial

In summary, denial can operate at four different levels: (1) lack of information, (2) conscious defensiveness, (3) unconscious defensiveness, or (4) delusion. It is important to evaluate which level of denial you are dealing with, because different interventions will be effective with different levels of denial.

Education about the target disorder is the most effective intervention for Lack of Information. Inner dialogue between the addictive self and the sober self is the most effective intervention for Conscious Defensiveness. Exposing the denial by using Denial Management Counseling is the best way to intervene when denial has become an unconscious defense mechanism. Psychotherapy and at times medication management is needed when denial has become a strong delusion, especially when the delusion is linked to other personality or mental disorders.

The use of denial, however, is not a problem that is unique to people with addictive or mental disorders. Everyone has a tendency to use denial when confronted with painful or overwhelming problems. Let's see how denial is a normal part of the human condition.

1–4. Denial and the Human Condition

Denial is a universal problem. All people tend to use denial when confronted with painful or overwhelming problems. To effectively manage denial we must be able to put the denial process into its proper context in relationship to people in general. Then we can apply the principles of denial to people experiencing specific problems, diseases, or disorders.

The relationship of denial to the human condition can be explained with a series of five basic assumptions about the nature of the human beings. These five basic assumptions act as the philosophical foundation of the Denial Management System. These assumptions are as follows: (1) As human beings, we are truth-seeking animals; (2) we are fallible and tend to make mistakes; (3) we have a tendency to lie to ourselves; (4) we have a tendency to lie to others; and (5) we need truth-seeking systems to protect us from our tendencies toward error, self-deception, and deceit. Let's look at each of these basic assumptions in more detail.

We Are Truth-Seeking Animals

As human beings we are, by our very nature, designed to seek the truth. Even the youngest of children have a basic need to make sense out of their world by explaining and assigning meaning to what they experience. This urge to find and comprehend the truth about our existence spawns a conscious stream of existential questions.

Truth-Seeking

1.   We are truth-seeking animals who continuously seek answers to the basic questions of life:
- **Identity:** Who am I?
- **Purpose:** Why am I here?
- **Belonging:** Where do I fit in?
- **Diagnosis:** What is wrong with me?
- **Recovery:** How can I get well?

First there is the question of identity: *Who am I?* Then there is the question of purpose: *Why am I here?* And then, the question of belonging: *How do I fit in?* What is my place in the world? And finally, the question of responsibility: *What does the world require of me in order to survive and thrive?*

When things go wrong or we experience frustration, pain, or disappointment we ask the question of diagnosis: *What is wrong with me?* And then we ask the question of recovery: *How can I get well? What must I do to eliminate my pain and suffering and live a meaningful life?*

We Tend to Make Mistakes

As human beings we are fallible. We are not perfect and have a tendency to make mistakes. We tend to make mistakes for several reasons. First, *the truth is hard to find.* The real world is a confusing place that does not come with an instruction manual. We have to figure out how things work.

We learn about the world in two ways: the teaching of others and personal trial and error. We all learn about the world from other people who teach us what they know. Sometimes they teach us *directly* by telling and showing us things. At other times they teach us *indirectly* through books, videotapes, or audiotapes. Our first teachers are usually our parents. Our parents, like us, are fallible human beings. As a result they may neglect to teach us some things we need to know. They may also teach us things they believe are true that, in fact, are not.

The other way we figure things out is by *trial and error.* We hear something, see someone, or do something. It seems like a good idea so we try it for ourselves. Sometimes what we try works and sometimes it doesn't. Either way, we learn from the consequences of what we do. If we try something and it works for us we tend to keep doing it. If we try something and it doesn't work for us, we tend to stop doing it and try something else. The problem is that some people, especially people who tend to get addicted, define something as working when it makes them feel good. They have a mistaken belief that goes like this: "If I do something and it makes me feel good, it works. If I do something else and it doesn't make me feel good, it doesn't work." Cognitive therapists call this thinking error *emotional reasoning*, and it is very common in chemically dependent people.

Some people get set in their ways. They believe that doing things a certain way "should work." Even when it doesn't they hold on to the belief that it should work the way they want it to, so they keep trying the same things and making the same mistakes over and over again. One definition of insanity goes like this: "Insanity is expecting different consequences from the same behavior."

Human Fallibility

We are fallible human beings
who tend to make mistakes because:

- The truth is difficult to find
- We learn about the world from other
  people who might be wrong
- We are programmed to learn
  by trial and error
- We confuse feeling good with
  knowing the truth

My father once explained the same principle in a different way. He said, *"A genius makes a mistake once, learns the lesson, and never makes the same mistake again. A smart person makes a mistake twice, learns the lesson, and never makes the same mistake again. An average person might make the mistake three times, learns the lesson, and never make the mistake again. A fool keeps making the same mistake over and over again, keeps blaming other people for the problem, and never learns the lesson the mistake is trying to teach him."* There is also an old proverb that drives this point home: "Fool me once, shame on you. Fool me twice, shame on me!"

Even though we have a natural tendency to make mistakes, few people like to admit it. So when we make a mistake we have a tendency to lie and try to persuade ourselves it wasn't really a mistake.

We Have a Tendency to Lie to Ourselves

As human beings we have a tendency to lie to ourselves. The human mind is capable of self-deception. This could be because we have a natural tendency to see things in a way that causes us the least pain and gives us the easiest solution or way out.

Self-deception

We have a tendency to lie to ourselves because:

- We like to see things in a way that causes the least pain and gives us the easiest solution or way out.

- We can become sincerely deluded by believing that our lies are true.

Wanting to take the easy way out is a normal and natural tendency in every human being. People who succeed learn to recognize that this desire for the easy way out is a defect of character or a self-defeating personality trait that needs to be overcome. Whenever they find themselves wanting to take the easier, softer way, they see it as a warning sign that they are setting themselves up to get into trouble. Then they consciously invest extra energy in figuring out what they really need to do in order to get the result they want. In other words, successful people learn to deal with the world the way it really is, not the way they would like it to be. They deal with the world on its own terms.

Successful people learn
to deal with the world the way it really is,
not the way they would like it to be.
They deal with the world on its own terms.

At times, we can start believing that the lies we tell ourselves are actually the truth. Some people call this being *sincerely deluded.* As we discussed, a delusion is a strong belief that something is true despite convincing evidence that it is not true. If we are deluded, we believe in the truth of our point of view despite evidence that we are wrong. We are basically saying to ourselves, *"I don't care what the facts are, my mind is made up."* We confuse how we want things to be with the way things really are. Then we come to believe in "the truth as I see it" and defend that "truth" when anyone tries to challenge it. The mechanism by which we lie to ourselves is called **irrational thinking.** We follow rules of thinking that prevent us from seeing the truth.

The mechanism of truth-seeking is called **rational thinking.** Rational thinking is *clear,* internally logical, and externally consistent. Our thinking is clear when we choose to be aware of exactly what we are thinking and work hard to clarify our thoughts. Our thinking is *logical* when our thoughts fit together and do not contradict each other because we choose to follow a consistent set of thinking or decision rules. Our thinking is *rational* when our clear, internally consistent thoughts match the objective realities of the world around us.

We can lie to ourselves by refusing to think clearly. We know that something is wrong, but choose not to focus on it. We choose not to think about it. We choose not to try and figure out what is going wrong.

We can lie to ourselves by using thoughts that contradict each other and then insisting that both are true. This is called developing an inconsistent internal logic system.

We can also lie to ourselves by attempting to use inaccurate explanations and understandings about the world around us. We expect the external world to conform to our inner wishes that describe the way we would like things to be instead of the way things are.

Once we develop "the truth as I see it" we tend to defend and protect that truth when others try to show us it might be wrong. This leads us to the fourth philosophical principle of denial management.

We Have a Tendency to Lie to Others

Once we become sincerely deluded as a result of believing

our own lies, we become "constitutionally incapable" of telling the truth. Why? Because we believe that our mistake is really the truth. Until we become willing to test, challenge, and change our mistaken beliefs, we will not be able to know when we are telling the truth and when we are not.

> **Deceit:** The tendency to lie to others when...
> • We are threatened
> • We believe it is in our best interest

Sometimes, however, people consciously and deliberately lie to others. The process of lying to others is called deceit. We are most likely to practice **deceit** when we are threatened or when we believe it is in our best interest to do so.

So then we must deal with the question of how we test out our beliefs to determine if they are actually true or if we are lying to ourselves. The answer is that we need to use truth-seeking systems. Denial Management Counseling (DMC) is a truth-seeking system. We will explore the concept of truth-seeking systems in the second half of the book on denial management. For now, let's look at the basic principles that govern or shape our tendencies to use denial.

1–5. The Principles that Govern Denial

If the four basic assumptions about the human condition are true, then we all have a tendency to deceive ourselves. This self-deception is what we refer to as denial. Because we are completing an in-depth exploration of denial, it is important to make explicit seven basic principles that are the foundation of denial management. These principles are as follows: (1) Denial is a normal psychological defense, (2) Denial blocks recognition and problem solving, (3) Acceptance and problem solving are antidotes for denial, (4) Denial can be recognized when activated, (5) Denial can be managed when recognized, (6) Problems can be solved when dealt with honestly and responsibly. Let's look at these six basic principles of denial management in more detail.

1. Denial Is a Normal Psychological Defense

Denial is a normal and natural psychological defense. Just as the human body has an immune system to protect it from dangerous physical organisms, the human mind has a *mental immune system* to protect it from overwhelming pain and problems. That mental immune system is called a psychological defense system or a psychological defensive structure. The goal of these psychological defenses is to protect the integrity of our mind and personality.

Denial is one part of this defensive system. Denial is activated whenever we are asked to think or talk about a painful or overwhelming problem. There is nothing pathological about this. It is a normal and natural human response to severe pain and problems.

Everyone uses denial every day. The brain has an automatic screening system called the Reticular Activating System (RAS) that forces it to block out certain perceptions that it is programmed to consider irrelevant. In states of normal stress, the brain locks on to signals that have *pay value* ("This is good for me") or *threat value* ("This is bad for me"). Everything else gets blocked out or unconsciously denied.

The RAS is programmed by the *values* integrated into our personality. Values are the things we believe are important enough to invest time, energy, and resources to acquire and maintain. The RAS is programmed to notice anything we have assigned value to. If we assign it a positive value, we can say the perception has pay value and the brain says, "This is good for me. I want it!" The perception is presented to the conscious mind along with the emotional urge to go get it.

Values

The things important enough to invest our time, energy, and resources to acquire and maintain.

The RAS is also programmed to notice anything that challenges our values. These things have threat value and the brain says "This is bad for me. I must get away from this or destroy it." So the perception is noticed and presented to the mind along with an emotional urge to get away from or destroy the threat. The emotional urge to get away from the threat is called *fear*. Fear ranges in intensity from mild anxiety to intense panic. The emotional urge to destroy the threat is called *anger*. Anger ranges in intensity from mild frustration to intense rage. *Violence* is the behavioral response to intense anger that is processed through a mistaken belief that "violence is an effective way to deal with this threat."

At times of high stress the brain can get emotionally overloaded. At these times the brain will activate automatic defenses, which we will call denial patterns. Each denial pattern is a primal biopsychological program that is turned on by a specific trigger that threatens something we value. As a severe problem causes intense stress, the brain turns on intense fear and/or anger. This activates a psychological program that starts mobilizing automatic defensive thoughts and the urge to use resistant behaviors.

The tapes that are activated send specific messages in the form of self-talk patterns or cognitive themes. Each denial pattern has a distinctive cognitive theme that can be used to recognize it once it is activated. Here is an example of the types of automatic thoughts that run through the mind once denial is activated. The five examples are related to the primary denial patterns we call **The Big Five.**

1. **Avoidance:** "Get away from this! Avoid it at all costs! Don't think about it! Don't talk about it! Focus on other things and you'll feel better."
2. **Absolute Denial:** "Don't acknowledge it, deny that it exists, and it will go away."
3. **Minimizing:** "Don't blow this thing out of proportion. Maybe it's not as bad as you think it is. Other people think it's worse than it really is. But it's really not that bad!"
4. **Rationalizing:** "There are good reasons for having this problem. Therefore it can't really hurt me. So what's the big deal?"
5. **Blaming:** "It's not my fault! I shouldn't have to deal with the consequences of someone else's problems. Because

I'm not responsible, I'll find the person who is and make them take care of it!"

Clients need to understand that these defensive reactions are normal and natural. It is also important to recognize that, as therapists, we may have the tendency to "pathologize" the denial process. We may tend to see patients who are using denial as being sick. This is especially true with alcoholics and drug addicts.

We forget that anyone who has a serious illness most likely will deny it. Imagine this: You are sitting in a training session and begin to feel a pain in your chest. The pain slowly starts getting worse. How bad will the pain have to get before you turn to the people near you and ask them to call an ambulance because you think you are having a heart attack? In most cases people have to hurt so bad that they pass out and fall on the floor. Even then, many of them may still resist help saying things like: "I'm fine!" "This will pass!" or "This couldn't be happening to me!"

Research shows that alcoholics and drug addicts have about the same level of denial as do people with cancer, heart disease, diabetes, and other chronic lifestyle-related problems. Denial is the biggest factor that blocks early identification and treatment of any chronic lifestyle-related disease.

Denial is also an important factor that stops people from maintaining necessary treatment. As soon as they feel better, people tend to stop the treatment regimen. Why? Because of a denial pattern called **Flight into Health.** When using flight into health we say something like this to ourselves: *"I feel better, therefore I must be better. And because I'm better, I don't need to continue my treatment!"*

I want to state again that this does not just happen with alcoholics, addicts, and people with mental disorders. It happens to anyone with a serious disease or illness or who is facing a painful or overwhelming problem. Denial has probably prevented each of us from following through on recommended treatment.

We all know that when we have an infection and are prescribed antibiotics we are supposed to complete the entire prescription, even if the symptoms go away and we start feeling better. How many of you, however, have a prescription bottle with some antibiotics left in it. Why didn't you finish it? Probably because when you started to feel better your denial caused you to stop. Denial is normal and natural. We all experience it. Learning to recognize and manage our denial is a normal developmental life task.

2. Denial Has Both Benefits and Disadvantages

There are both benefits and disadvantages to using denial. The major benefit of denial is that it helps people deal with unbearable pain and overwhelming problems. If you don't believe it, talk to people who were near death as a result of a serious illness or injury and then survived. Ask them if at their worst moment they realized how sick and close to death they were. Most people will tell you they didn't. It was only as they began getting well that they realized just how sick they were. Why? Because at the moment of greatest illness, denial can be very strong and help us keep hope alive by preventing us from seeing how hopeless the situation is.

Benefits and Disadvantages of Denial

1. **Benefits of Denial:** Denial is a *gift* that helps people deal with unbearable pain and overwhelming problems.

2. **Disadvantages of Denial:** Denial is a *curse* that keeps people from seeing what is wrong and taking appropriate action.

The major disadvantage of denial is that it prevents people from seeing what is wrong and taking appropriate action to handle the situation. When I was about ten years old my father had a friend named Al who had serious diabetes. Al refused to regulate his diet, manage his stress, or take his insulin. Why? Because Al was convinced his doctor was wrong. *"I don't have diabetes!"* he would say over and over again. *"I have a circulatory problem in my fingers and toes that makes them hurt."* Al was certain the "crazy doctors" didn't know what they were talking about. Because he refused to manage his diabetes, Al kept getting sicker. Before he died he had to have both arms and legs amputated because of his "circulation problem." Right up until his death Al insisted he did not have diabetes. His diabetes would have been manageable if only he could have learned to manage his denial.

3. Denial Blocks Recognition and Problem Solving

If we don't learn how to recognize and manage our tendency to use denial, it can prevent us from recognizing and solving important problems. Denial of a problem can create more serious consequences than the problem itself. Denial, a normal and natural defense mechanism designed to protect us from pain and problems, can backfire and cause us to experience more pain and problems.

4. Acceptance and Problem Solving Are Antidotes for Denial

Fortunately there are two antidotes for denial: acceptance and problem solving. **The first antidote for denial is a peaceful acceptance of the truth.** If we can calmly face the problem, acknowledge the truth about what is going on, and accept that it is happening we can then develop a way for handling the situation. This peaceful acceptance shows up in our ability to stay centered and connected with our feelings while thinking about and talking about serious problems. It is the ability to calmly face and affirm the truth even if we don't like it. People who have accepted the truth about a serious problem have the ability to honestly say to themselves, *"I have a serious problem. I am responsible for dealing with it. I'm willing to learn how."*

> Whether or not you were responsible for causing the problem, you are now responsible for solving it.

Notice that the person may or may not be responsible for causing the problem. Addiction, like many other serious diseases and disorders, has multiple and complex causes. Some of these causes were within the control of our clients and some were not. The important point is this: *Whether or not you were responsible for causing the problem, you are now responsible for solving it.* You own the problem and it is yours and yours alone. You are responsible for dealing with it whether you like it or not. As a matter of fact, you have no choice but to deal with the problem. The only choice is whether you will deal with the problem effectively or ineffectively.

The effective management of any problem requires that you know what the problem is. In other words, you must be able to recognize and manage your own denial. You must be able to see the truth before you can take effective action. Therefore, we are all responsible for learning how to manage our own denial so we can see what is truly wrong with us and develop an effective plan for dealing with it.

The second antidote for denial is problem solving. Once people recognize and accept their problems, they must learn to use effective problem-solving strategies. Here is a six-step systematic process you can use to solve the problem once your clients have recognized and accepted what the problem is:

Step 1: Problem Identification: Figure out what the problem is.

Step 2: Problem Clarification: Define the problem and identify the thoughts, feelings, urges, and behaviors you use that tend to make the problem worse.

Step 3: Identify Alternative Solutions: Think of as many possible ways to solve the problem as you can.

Step 4: Project the Logical Consequences of Each Alternative: Imagine yourself using each alternative solution and ask yourself three questions: If I try to solve the problem using this alternative solution, (1) What is the best thing that could happen? (2) What is the worst thing that could happen? and (3) What is the most likely thing that will happen? Projecting the logical consequence of each alternative solution asks a person to "think it through before they act it out."

Step 5: Decision: Choose one of the alternative solutions that you believe will work for you. Make a decision about what you are going to do.

Step 6: Action: Put your decision into action. Remember the saying, "If nothing changes, nothing changes! Easy does it, but do it."

The need to use denial will go down when you recognize and accept the problem and develop an effective problem solving plan.

5. Denial Can Be Recognized when Activated

People can learn to recognize their denial when it is activated. They can recognize the increased physical stress, the sudden onset of anger or fear, the common self-talk that starts running through their mind, what they say when talking with others, and what they are doing.

Many people learn to recognize and manage denial through the role modeling of their parents. No one ever tells them, "I'm going to teach you how to recognize and manage your denial so you can face the truth of a situation." They just observe and mimic their parents' behaviors.

Unfortunately, many people were raised in dysfunctional families by parents who habitually used denial as a preferred coping tool. They didn't think there was anything wrong with it. People raised in these kinds of families learn to deny reality from their parents. Instead of learning how to recognize and manage denial so they could see the truth, they learned to become masters at self-deception by using sophisticated denial patterns as an automatic and unconscious way of dealing with pain and problems.

6. Denial Can Be Managed when Recognized

Denial can be managed when it is recognized. Using denial is a habit. The principles used in changing any habit can be applied to recognizing and managing denial. Not only can we learn how to manage denial. We must learn to manage it *well*, especially if we have a chronic, lifestyle-related disease or disorder that could destroy our lives.

7. Problems Can Be Solved when Dealt with Honestly and Responsibly

We can solve most problems if we recognize the truth about

what is happening. Even those we can't solve, we can learn to manage better. An important goal of denial management is to teach people how to honestly face the truth about what is going wrong so they can learn how to manage their problems more effectively.

> Denial management teaches people how to face the truth about what is going wrong so they can learn how to manage their problems more effectively.

One of the first things to do with people who are using strong denial and resistance is to present and discuss the basic principles of denial management. The next step is to explain an assessment process that can be used as a personal inventory for finding out the truth about what is wrong. It is important to establish a collaborative relationship with your clients by asking them to work with you to figure out the truth about what is wrong and the best, most effective way to deal with the truth. In other words, ask your clients to accept Denial Management Counseling (DMC) as a truth-seeking tool.

The first step in the process of repairing a damaged life is to recognize and accept the truth about what is wrong. The problem is that people in denial will try to assert that nothing is wrong in the face of overwhelming and undeniable evidence that something is very wrong. To counter this tendency, I often suggest that my clients experiment with telling me about their problems by starting with the words, *"Here's what I believe is really happening, but I might be wrong."* This affirmation helps them both acknowledge what they currently believe and accept themselves as fallible human beings who may have based that belief on a mistake. This way of thinking opens them to the possibility of personal error and creates a willingness to hear another point of view.

1–6. Denial Patterns

Denial Patterns are automatic and unconscious ways of perceiving, thinking, feeling, and acting that prevent people from recognizing, accurately assessing the seriousness of, or accepting responsibility for solving problems.

There are twelve commonly used denial patterns. To make it easier to remember and work with them, we are going to divide the denial patterns into two groups: The Big Five and the Small Seven. In this section we will briefly review all of the common denial patterns to give you a feel for what they are and general ways they can be managed effectively. We also show you how the denial patterns can be used together to form more complicated *denial strategies* that clients use to keep their therapist off balance. Later in the book we will examine each denial pattern in more detail and give specific examples of how to use Denial Management Counseling (DMC) to directly deal with each denial pattern.

The Big Five Denial Patterns

I call the five most commonly used denial patterns the Big Five. In my experience these are the denial patterns that are most commonly used by clients. This means that the Big Five will be the denial patterns you will have to deal with most frequently. The Big Five are Avoidance, Absolute Denial, Minimizing, Rationalizing, and Blaming. Let's look at each in more detail.

The Big Five Denial Patterns

1. **Avoidance:** "I'll talk about anything but the real problem!"
2. **Absolute Denial:** "No, not me!"
3. **Minimizing:** "It's not that bad!"
4. **Rationalizing:** "I have a good reason!"
5. **Blaming:** "It's not my fault!"

---

1. Avoidance—"I'll talk about anything but the problem!"

The cognitive theme of avoidance is, "I'll talk about anything but the real problem!" People using avoidance refuse to directly answer questions and try to shift the focus to interesting but irrelevant issues. There are a number of common variations to the avoidance denial pattern.

Avoidance by saying nothing is used to keep the real problem from coming up in conversation. People don't volunteer any information and when asked, they say little or nothing about the problem. The therapist is invited to start pulling information out of the client and, of course, this gives the client the opportunity to resist and say that the therapist is "sticking a nose into their personal business where it doesn't belong!"

Avoidance by Distraction is used to bring up other interesting things that are not related to the core problem in an attempt to get the therapist to follow along on a tour of interesting but irrelevant things.

Avoidance by Uproar is used to create conflicts or fights with the therapist that will shift the focus from the core problem to the conflict. By fighting, clients can avoid focusing on the core problems. They can also use the therapist's anger and aggressiveness as justification for leaving therapy.

Avoidance by Playing Dumb is used to convince the therapist they don't know what is going on when they really do. Therapists are invited to try to explain things endlessly while the client strategically fails to understand what the therapist means.

2. Absolute Denial—"No, not me!"

The cognitive theme of absolute denial is "No, not me! I don't have a problem!" When using absolute denial people tend to say there is nothing wrong when there is clear evidence that something is wrong. They do this by focusing their attention on creating a long list of reasons why the problem can't exist. The therapist is invited to try and convince the client that they have a serious problem. Then clients can disagree with the therapist and feel insulted by what the therapist is telling them.

3. Minimizing—"It's not that bad!"

The cognitive theme of minimizing is "Yes, I have a problem, but it isn't that bad!" When minimizing, people tend to say the problem is very minor and other people are just blowing it out of proportion and making a big deal out of it for no reason. When people start minimizing, progress has been made. They now accept that they have a problem and they are simply arguing about how bad the problem is. The therapist is invited to underestimate the seriousness of the problem and focus on why other people are taking a relatively minor issue and blowing it out of proportion.

4. Rationalizing—"I have a good reason!"

The cognitive theme of rationalizing is "Yes, it is a serious problem, but I have a good reason for having the problem." When using rationalizing, people tend to believe the problem doesn't count, so there should be no consequences because there are good reasons for having it. The therapist is invited to focus on the reasons for having the problem instead of focusing on how to solve the problem.

5. Blaming—"It's not my fault!"

The cognitive theme of blaming is "Somebody else caused the problem, so it's not my fault!" Blaming is based on the irrational belief that "If I can prove that someone else is responsible for my problem, I won't experience any adverse consequences and will not have to do anything to solve the problem." The therapist is invited to shift the focus from the problem itself to the search for who is responsible for causing the problems. The therapist and the client can then spend time arguing about who's at fault instead of clarifying the problem and developing problem-solving strategies.

The Small Seven Denial Patterns

Let's look next at the Small Seven Denial Patterns. People use the Small Seven Denial Patterns less often in treatment, but you will see them frequently enough to warrant being prepared to recognize and manage them.

The Small Seven Denial Patterns

6. **Comparing:** "Others are worse than me."

7. **Compliance:** "I'll say anything you want to hear if you leave me alone!"

8. **Manipulating:** "I'll only recover if you do what I want."

9. **Flight into Health:** "Feeling better means that I am better."

10. **Recovery by Fear:** "Being scared will get me well."

11. **Strategic Hopelessness:** "Because nothing will work I don't have to try."

12. **Democratic Disease State:** "I have the right to kill myself!"

6. Comparing—"Others are worse than me"

The first of the Small Seven is comparing. When people use comparing they tend to think something like this: "I can't possibly need to stop drinking or using drugs because I know other people who use more alcohol and drugs and who have much worse problems than I do." The basic mistaken belief is, "If someone else is worse than I am it proves that I don't have a problem."

7. Compliance—"I'll say anything you want if you leave me alone!"

The second of the Small Seven is compliance. People are in compliance when they pretend to solve the problem in order to be left alone. The cognitive theme of compliance is, "I'll say anything you want to hear if you leave me alone." The mistaken belief that drives compliance is, "If I can get people to leave me alone by going through the motions of solving the problem, the problem will go away."

People who use compliance tend to believe the real problem is that other people are forcing them to deal with the problem. The irrationality goes like this: "The real problem really isn't the problem. The only problem I have is that people are forcing me to deal with the problem. If people would just leave me alone the problem will go away. The best way to get them to leave me alone is to convince them I'll do what they want me to do."

8. Manipulating—"I'll only recover if you do what I want"

The third of the Small Seven is manipulating. When people use manipulation they try to get other people to do things for them that they can and should do for themselves. People who are manipulating tend to think something like this: "I'll admit I have a problem if you handle it for me without forcing me to change." The mistaken belief is, "If I can get someone else to solve my problem, I won't have to do anything to solve my own problems." Unfortunately, there are certain problems that we must solve on our own.

Let's suppose my problem is that I'm really thirsty. I go to my therapist, tell her all about my problem, and then ask, "*Will you please go and take a big drink of water for me?*" Even if she would do it for me, it would not relieve my thirst. Imagine further if I would then accuse the therapist of being a bad therapist because no matter how much water she drank for me, I was still thirsty.

9. Flight into Health—"Feeling better means that I am better"

The third of the Small Seven is flight into health. Here people believe,"If I feel better, I am better!" They also mistakenly believe, "If I know what is wrong, my problem will automatically and magically be fixed." This is because one of the things that makes them feel better is understanding what is wrong with them. So people using flight into health say something like this to themselves: "What a relief. I feel so much better knowing what is wrong. And because I feel better, therefore I must be better. And because I'm better, I don't need to continue my treatment!" They tend to think, "Now that I know what the problem is, it will go away. I'm cured!" The mistaken belief that drives flight into health goes like this: "Knowledge alone, without action, will solve my problem."

10. Recovery by Fear—"Being scared will let me get well"

The fourth of the Small Seven is called recovery by fear.

The theme of this denial pattern is that being really scared about drinking and drugging will keep me abstinent. The mistaken belief is, "My addiction problems will be solved if I get scared enough about what will happen if I don't solve it." People using this denial pattern think something like this: "I'll never do it again because I'm too scared of the consequences. Fear alone will keep me sober and solve my problems!"

The problem is that people often drink and use drugs to handle their fear. Intense fear can also impair judgment and cause people to make mistakes or become immobilized. Fear makes you afraid. It is a warning sign that something is wrong. Fear, however, doesn't solve anything.

11. Strategic Hopelessness—"Because nothing works, I don't have to try"

The sixth of the Small Seven is strategic hopelessness. People using this denial pattern play hopeless in order to convince others to stop trying to help. The cognitive theme is, "I've tried everything and nothing has worked. I'm hopeless and you can't help me. So leave me alone."

The mistaken belief that drives strategic hopelessness is this, "If I can convince you I am hopeless, you will leave me alone and my problem will be solved." The mistaken belief is similar to what drives compliance: "The only real problem I have is that you are forcing me to face problems I can't solve. The problems aren't the real problem. You are the real problem. If you would leave me alone my problems would be solved."

People who initially use compliance ("I'll pretend to do what you want in order to get you to leave me alone") will often shift into strategic hopelessness ("I've tried to do everything you suggested and nothing has worked. I'm hopeless, so leave me alone and let me suffer in peace.").

12. Democratic Disease State—"I have the right to kill myself!"

The last of the Small Seven is the democratic disease state. People using this denial pattern believe they have a right to be addicted and act out in self-destructive ways, and no one has a right to stop them. The cognitive theme is this: "I have a right to drink, use drugs, be addicted, destroy my life, and die. It's none of your business. You don't have the right to make me stop!"

The mistaken belief that drives the democratic disease state is this: "Because I have the right to drink and drug myself to death, I should be left alone to die in peace." The mistaken belief is that addiction will end in a peaceful death. It doesn't. Addiction is one of the most painful and humiliating ways to die.

Denial Strategies—How the Denial Patterns Work Together

Clients don't use denial patterns one at a time; they use them strategically, shifting from one to another in order to keep the therapist confused and off balance. As soon as the client senses the therapist is recognizing and learning to effectively deal with one denial pattern, they switch to another. Most clients develop a predictable strategy of switching from one denial pattern to another. When they come to an end of the learned sequence they typically start again and recycle through the same sequence of denial patterns.

This is why it is important to keep two goals in mind. The first goal is to recognize the specific denial pattern the client is using. The second goal is to notice the sequence in which the client uses the denial patterns. This sequence is called the *denial strategy.*

One of the reasons for organizing the denial patterns around the concept of the Big Five and the Small Seven is because the Big Five Denial Patterns are the most common ones used as building blocks of the overall denial strategy.

Here is an example of how one of my clients, I'll call him John, used the Big Five Denial Patterns in sequence to form a complex strategy to keep him from recognizing and taking personal responsibility for the problems related to his alcohol and other drug use.

John started out by using avoidance. He wanted to talk about anything but the problem. I recognized the avoidance and deliberately kept a relentless focus on identifying and clarifying John's presenting problems. This failed several times so I tried to expose and consciously deal with the avoidance denial pattern. At this point John got annoyed and moved from avoidance into absolute denial. He was suddenly willing to talk about his presenting problem—his arrest for Driving under the Influence of Alcohol (DUI). He said, *"OK, I understand that I was referred for DUI,"* but he gave the clear message that he didn't have a drinking problem. *"It's all a mistake,"* he asserted. *"I had a couple of social drinks but I have never had a drinking problem! How could you accuse me of such a thing?"*

When I recognized the absolute denial, I reviewed the police report and other documented evidence and tried to present John with an overwhelming and undeniable argument that the DUI was real and that it was related to an episode of alcohol abuse. John kept dismissing the evidence as irrelevant. I began to expose the absolute denial pattern, but once again, before I could expose and consciously deal with it, John shifted the denial pattern again, this time into minimizing. He said, *"OK, the DUI is a problem, but it's not that bad. It's just that other people are blowing it up all out of proportion."*

I explored this with him for a while, but he was adamant that the arrest was based on a misunderstanding and his attorney would be able to handle it easily. I noticed John's attempt to invite me back into avoidance by trying to find out who these "other people" were. Instead, I focused on objectively evaluating the seriousness of the problem by using a ten-point scale and comparing the DUI to other common life problems. John refused to work with me. *"That's stupid!"* he told me. *"I told you that it's not that bad. What good would it do to use a ten-point scale to tell you the same thing I've been trying to tell you for the last hour?"*

I felt angry with his condescending attitude but avoided the invitation to move into avoidance by uproar. I focused on trying to expose and consciously deal with the minimizing pattern when John shifted again, this time to rationalizing.

"There are good reasons for what happened to me," John asserted. *"You just don't understand why these things are happening!"* I noticed that John was inviting me to accept a vague, general description of his problems as "what happened" and "these things

that are happening to me." I asked John to clarify what he meant, but he was insistent on telling me about the "good reasons" why he had these vague, unspecified problems.

Notice that John had not clarified the problem (due to avoidance). He also had not accepted personal responsibility for having the problem (due to absolute denial). John never even acknowledged that the problem was serious enough to warrant an investment of time or energy to solve it (due to minimizing). Instead he wanted to pursue an in-depth discussion of the reasons why he had these vague, unspecified problems.

I listened to several of the rationalizations and then began to expose the rationalizing pattern when suddenly John shifted his focus again. This time he went into blaming. He started to get angry as he described how the DUI problem was not his fault. *"I was set up by that cop,"* he said. *"I'm really the victim here."* John then started telling me how the law needed to be changed and that the only way this problem could be solved was by holding the police responsible for unfairly interfering in his private life. John wanted me to put the responsibility where it really belonged—on someone else.

I refused John's invitation to participate with him in bashing the police. I started to expose the blaming denial pattern so we could consciously deal with it. John suddenly shifted the focus again, this time back into avoidance. He wanted to discuss the legal problems with the DUI laws. He was also interested in how he could help his wife settle down. She was so upset he got arrested that she wouldn't sleep with him. He was curious about what her problem might be. Then the cycle started all over again.

This cycle of denial can be frustrating. Almost every therapist experiences it on a fairly regular basis. Some get stuck in this cycle with their clients for weeks or months of therapy. Denial Management Counseling (DMC) was designed to give therapists a way to stop this process in its tracks and get clients to focus on identifying, clarifying, and solving the core problems that brought them into treatment.

Distinguishing Denial from Antisocial Personality

Before we move into a detailed description of Denial Management Counseling (DMC), I want to spend some time looking at the difference between denial and the symptoms of Antisocial Personality Disorder (ASPD). To do this we need to briefly discuss three terms: antisocial personality disorder (ASPD), psychopathy, and sociopathy. Although the three terms generally refer to the same types of psychological problems and are often used interchangeably, it is helpful to define each.

ASPD is the title of a DSM-IV personality disorder that focuses primarily on clients who repeatedly engage in behaviors that break the law and violate social norms or conventions. People with ASPD tend to challenge authority, break rules, and victimize others. When caught by the consequences they tend to feel little or no guilt or remorse, deny personal responsibility, and blame the victim or enforcer for causing the problem. As a result, they fail to learn from experience.

The terms psychopath and sociopath include the symptoms of ASPD but also focus on the manipulative personality style that sets the stage for the antisocial behavior and their response to getting caught. The concept of psychopathy focuses on superficial charm, duplicitousness, and deceptiveness. Let's briefly look at each of the symptoms.

Antisocial Personality Traits

1. Superficially Charming
2. Duplicitous
3. Deceptive
4. Challenges Authority
5. Breaks Rules
6. Victimizes Others
7. Feels No Guilt
8. Denies Responsibility
9. Blames Victim/Enforcer
10. Does not Learn from Experience
11. Abuse of Alcohol and other Drugs
12. Socially Conforming

Superficially Charming: People with ASPD tend to be charming and likable. They are good at quickly sizing people up, figuring out what they want to hear and see, and giving them what they want. In this way they can invite people to like the image they portray and create a sense of safety, trust, and confidence that allows them to take advantage of and use people later.

Duplicitous: The term duplicitous means two-faced, or appearing to be one way while actually being another. Duplicitous people present themselves in two different ways. There is a public self they present in order to manipulate and deceive others and there is the private self that is self-serving and callous to the needs of others. This private antisocial self is kept hidden.

Deceptive: People with ASPD tell lies. They don't tell the whole truth and mix partial truths with big lies to confuse people and to create a sense of trust in their honesty. They are convincing liars who appear to genuinely believe everything they say. People with ASPD don't just make mistakes, they craft complex patterns of lies to entrap other people and shift blame and responsibility if caught.

Challenges Authority: People with ASPD believe they are the ultimate authority. In other words they believe there is no authority higher than they are and that they have the right to set rules and hold other people accountable to them.

Breaks Rules: People with ASPD believe they are above the law. As a result they constantly break rules. They believe other people are obligated to follow the rules they set, but they don't have to follow any rules and keep any agreements. They continuously make and break promises and are unwilling and often unable to keep their word.

Victimizes Others: People with ASPD tend to victimize others. Other people are things or objects put in the world for them to use. They don't see people as individuals with feelings and rights. If someone meets their needs in the moment, they will treat them well. As soon as the person fails to do what they want when they want, people with ASPD feel betrayed and either discard or abuse the person who isn't what they wanted them to be.

Feels No Guilt: When caught by the consequences, people with ASPD tend to feel little or no guilt or remorse. This is because people with ASPD are operating at very low levels of moral development. Their battle cry is, "If it feels good in the moment, it is good. If it feels bad in the moment, it is bad." Because they believe they never do anything wrong, there is no need to ever feel guilty.

Denies Responsibility: When caught by the consequences people with ASPD tend to deny personal responsibility. In the minds of people with ASPD, nothing is ever their fault. People with ASPD do not believe they are responsible for the logical consequences of their behavior. They believe there should be no consequences. As one client told me, "I'm immune from bad consequences, or at least I should be!"

Blames Victim/Enforcer: When caught by the consequences, people with ASPD tend to blame the victim or enforcer for causing their problem. They say things like, "I would have never gotten into trouble if the victim didn't scream so loud, if the officer who arrested me would have cut me some slack, and if the judge who sentenced me would have been more fair." In their mind any adverse consequences are caused because other people are victimizing them. This gives them the right to protect themselves by fighting back against those who they see as hurting them.

Does Not Learn from Experience: People with ASPD live in the here and now. They seek immediate thrills and gratification. They don't reflect on the past or try to project logical consequences into the future. When problems develop or bad things happen they tend to blame others and fail to see how those consequences had anything to do with who they are or what they were doing. As a result they usually fail to learn from experience and keep repeating the same pattern of self-defeating behaviors despite the consequences.

Abuse of Alcohol and Other Drugs: People with ASPD often abuse or are addicted to alcohol and other mood-altering drugs, both legal and illicit. Their desire for quick money often leads them into the illegal drug trade. Their insensitivity to others and tendency to feel little or no guilt or remorse allow them to move easily into patterns of crime and violence.

Socially Conforming: There are socially conforming psychopaths who are highly manipulative and use and abuse other people, but they do so without overtly breaking the law or getting caught. Because of their intelligence and ability to be cunning and ruthless, many socially conforming psychopaths can rise to high positions in government and business. When they do, they don't break the rules, they change the rules to benefit themselves even if it hurts others.

Because there are many psychopaths who are addicted and have other mental disorders, it is important to keep these basic characteristics in mind. If you see these signs in your client, be aware they may be suffering from far more than just denial. They may be locked into an antisocial or psychopathic delusional system. If you see these warning signs make sure to get a good personality assessment as soon as possible. The denial management techniques being presented here will only work with a person having an antisocial disorder if they are used in the context of treating that disorder. Many therapists fail with clients because they mistake the symptoms of antisocial disorder with denial.

Turning Denial On and Off

There are triggers that activate or turn on denial. There are also triggers that deactivate or turn it off. Let's explore the triggers that turn denial on and off in more detail.

Triggers for Denial

1. **Denial is turned on by...**
   - *thinking* and *talking* about painful problems.
2. **Denial is turned off by...**
   - taking the focus off the problem by thinking and talking about other things
   - teaching the client how to manage the pain caused by thinking and talking about the problem
   - solving the problem that causes the pain
3. **Denial is turned off by...**
   - managing the feelings that drive it.

1. Denial Is Turned On by Thinking about or Talking about Painful Problems: This makes it easy to predict that most clients will experience denial when completing an intake or assessment process. This is because we are asking them to think about and talk about painful problems. This virtually guarantees that denial and resistant behavior will be turned on.

2. Denial Is Turned Off by Thinking or Talking about Other Things: The easiest way to turn off denial is to start thinking about or talking about something else. As we saw earlier, this process is called *avoidance*. Remember this: people will have no need for denial if they are not thinking or talking about painful problems. Therefore, the first goal of every client with severe denial is to focus on something else. They are willing to think and talk about almost anything except the core painful problem that is forcing them to come into treatment.

3. Denial Is Turned Off by Managing the Feelings that Drive It: The feelings of pain, anger, fear, guilt, and shame drive denial. People in denial feel *pain* because they are facing a difficult and overwhelming problem that is destroying their life. They feel *anger* because it seems unfair and there is nothing they can do about. They feel *fear* because they are out of control and don't know how to handle the problem. They feel *guilt* because they believe the reason they are having the painful problems is because they are doing something wrong. They feel *shame* because they believe they are somehow defective for having the problem.

The Emotional Drivers of Denial

1. **Pain:** "I hurt so bad I can't stand it."
2. **Anger:** "My pain is unfair and there is nothing I can do about it."
3. **Fear:** "I'm out of control and I don't know what to do."
4. **Guilt:** "I believe I'm doing something wrong."
5. **Shame:** "I feel I am a defective person."

The antidote to these feelings is a sense of detached peacefulness that is often called acceptance or "being centered." It is not enough to teach a person how to recognize and label the emotional drivers of denial. We need to teach them to recognize and activate the feelings of detached peacefulness. To be peacefully detached doesn't mean you don't feel the feeling. It means that you develop the capacity to feel the feeling without it activating irrational thinking and physical stress responses that intensify the feelings.

Clients often report that when they are centered they can find a calm place of strength within themselves that can contain their feelings. Many people working Twelve Step programs achieve this state by "turning over" their feelings to a Higher Power. People using more traditional spiritual beliefs contain their feelings within a framework of sacrifice and of willingly facing and integrating the pain.

In all cases, clients I have talked to who have achieved the centered state report two key features: (1) they are able to keep their body relaxed while the feelings are experienced; and (2) they are able to keep their thoughts focused and avoid activating automatic irrational thinking patterns. This means that denial management involves teaching clients how to stay physically relaxed and consciously in control of their thinking when they are experiencing intense feelings.

Denial Management

Teaching clients how to stay physically relaxed and consciously in control of their thinking when they are experiencing intense feelings

Part 2

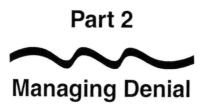

Managing Denial

Denial Management Counseling (DMC) is a systematic process for teaching people how to recognize and manage their denial so they can find the truth about what is wrong. Denial management teaches people how to find out what is going wrong in their lives. This is done by teaching them how to think and talk about their problems while staying calm, centered, and connected with their feelings. If denial is activated, they learn how to recognize it and turn it off so they can continue to focus on solving their primary problems.

Denial Management Counseling (DMC)

A systematic process for teaching people
how to recognize and manage their denial

2–1: An Introduction to Denial Management

Denial Management teaches people how to *find out the truth about what is going wrong with their lives and what they need to do in order to fix it.* At the beginning of this truth-seeking process, most people don't know what the truth is. Clients know that something is wrong but don't have a clear or accurate understanding of exactly what their problems are. At the start of treatment, therapists don't know what is wrong with their clients. What most therapists do know is how to guide their clients through a process that will help them discover the truth for themselves.

Our job as therapists is to develop a **collaborative relationship** with our clients in order to help them find out the truth about what is wrong. This means that we must keep an open mind, even when working with people exhibiting hard-core denial and resistance.

The first two issues that need to be raised with our clients are (1) Do you want to know the truth about what is going on in your life? and (2) Are you willing to use a systematic process to find the truth?

Critical Issues in Denial Management

1. Do you want to know the truth?
2. Are you willing to use a systematic process to find it?

Many clients believe that we, as therapists, have already made up our minds and prejudged them. They don't believe that we are interested in finding out what is really going on. They think we have a preestablished agenda and that the best way for them to deal with the situation is to figure out what we want so they can give it to us. Our clients are, in essence, asking us, *"What do you want me to say?"* The most helpful response that therapists can make is, *"I want you to tell me the truth."* Many clients respond by saying something like, *"So you think that I'm lying?"* An effective response is, *"No, I don't think you're lying. But at this point, I don't know you very well and I certainly don't know what the truth is. I'd like for us to work together to find out what's going on and what can be done to make things better."* If you are going to say this to your clients, you have to mean it. This means starting the therapy process without any preconceived ideas and working with your clients to accurately describe the truth about what is going on.

Denial management is a systematic process for finding the truth. By using a denial management system, people learn how to recognize and manage their own denial by using a system for self-assessment that forces them to think and talk about their problems, and to draw accurate conclusions about what is wrong and what needs to be done to solve them. The way to reduce denial and resistance is to stop trying to force people to tell you the truth, and start teaching them how to use a systematic process to figure out for themselves what the truth really is. Remember, people are truth-seeking animals. We all want to know what's really going on. The problem is that the truth is difficult to find. This is why we need truth-seeking systems to protect us from error and self-deception. The denial management process is a truth-seeking system.

> Trying to convince people of something
> they don't want to believe will only increase denial and resistance.
>
> To stop denial we must have a system
> that allows people to discover the truth for themselves.

Denial management teaches people how to think and talk about their problems without activating denial. Notice that effective denial management systems include both **a thinking process** and **a communication process**. Most people who are in denial can't see the truth because they are not thinking clearly, logically, and rationally. They are locked into automatic and unconscious modes of defensive thinking designed to help them deal with the pain and create the illusion that they are in control and effectively managing the problem.

Denial is the last refuge of the incompetent. When we have no other way to handle pain and problems we activate defensive ways of thinking. This is an automatic and unconscious response to intense pain and overwhelming problems that make us feel helpless. When we can get our clients to focus on learning how to use an effective and systematic process for figuring out what is wrong and what can be done to improve the situation, they feel more in control and their need to use denial goes down.

> Denial is the last refuge of the incompetent.
> When we have no other way to handle pain and problems we use defensive ways of thinking.

So remember: *focus on the process of finding the truth.* Don't try to confront the client with "the truth as the therapist sees it." Be patient and guide your clients through a process that will allow them to see the truth for themselves.

Denial management teaches clients how to stay calm and centered while thinking and talking about their problems. The phrase "being centered" can be used interchangeably with phrases like "being balanced," "being aware of your feelings yet detached," and "being integrated." The first key to staying centered while thinking about and talking about painful problems is to get calm and relaxed before you start. This means having some skill at **conscious relaxation.**

> Denial management teaches clients
> how to stay centered while thinking and talking
> about their problems.

It is often helpful to point out to your clients that they appear to be very stressed. You can say something like this: *"You seem to be very concerned about what's going on and I don't blame you. Most people would be really stressed if they were in your position. I'd like to help you relax and get centered. Then we can calmly look at what's going on, and figure what we can do about it."*

Then you can ask the client to rate their stress on a ten-point scale, with ten being the most stressed and zero being the least stressed. Ask, *"How much stress are you feeling right now?"* Then ask, *"Why do you rate your stress level that way?"* This process will get the client talking about their inner experiences. Then ask the client, *"What do you normally do to relax when you are stressed out?"* You can then say something like, *"In my experience people are a lot better at solving their problems if they can stay relaxed and centered. Is there anything you can you do right now would help you relax and get centered so that we can calmly look at what's going on?"*

This often opens the door for you to show the client how to use some simple **immediate relaxation techniques** like deep breathing, muscle tensing and relaxing, body scanning, or relaxation affirmations.

It is important to begin shifting the focus from confronting clients with the painful truth to helping clients cope with the stress and pain they are experiencing. It's also important to begin putting the responsibility on the client to manage their own thoughts, feelings, and behaviors while in the session. As they begin to understand that stress management is the first step of emotional self-regulation, they can begin to feel better and get more in control of themselves, even before the problem is identified, clarified, and resolved.

Denial Management Shifts the Focus...

- **from** confronting clients with the painful truth
- **to** helping clients cope with their immediate stress and pain.

Here is a warning. Clients experiencing strong denial and treatment resistance will unconsciously invite you to get stressed and emotionally upset. They want you to get frustrated and angry, because once you start acting out in response to their anger or pain they can blame you for their problems and use your reactions as an excuse to drop out of therapy. Fortunately, you don't have to accept the invitation to get upset. You can use the same immediate relaxation techniques that you teach clients to keep yourself centered and calm.

The Goal of Denial Management

To teach people how to stay calm and centered while thinking and talking about painful problems without using denial

To solve a problem we must be able to think and talk about it without experiencing denial. There are several conditions that must be met for this to happen. First, the therapist needs to stay calm and centered. The therapist must be able to recognize and refuse the invitations from their clients to get upset. Second, the therapist needs to learn how to shift responsibility to the client within the immediate context of the session for managing their own feelings, emotions, and behaviors. The client must be held accountable for managing their own behavior in the session. Third, the therapist needs to have a systematic approach based on proven principles and practices for helping their client to relax, get centered, and begin looking at what is really wrong.

2–2: Confrontation in the Management of Denial

Effective denial management requires the proper use of confrontation. Therapists who use confrontation effectively tend to be supportive, directive, and strategically honest. *Supportive* means that effective therapists support the client as a person. They find something about their clients they can like, respect, admire, and empathize with. They communicate with the client in a way that makes these positive strengths visible to their clients. *Directive* means that effective therapists have a process or system they use to evaluate what is wrong and to develop goals and treatment strategies. Directive therapists give the client a clear plan and a set of skills for recovery. They don't let their clients take total charge of the clinical process. *Strategic honesty* gives the effective therapist the ability to directly and clearly give the client feedback. This feedback focuses on exposing and reinforcing the clients hidden strengths while pointing out self-defeating ways of thinking, behaving, and living.

Therapists who use effective confrontation walk a razor's edge between **nondirective therapy methods** that allow clients in denial to turn their therapists into codependent enablers and **psychonoxious confrontation,** which ignores clients' strengths while continuously and relentlessly pointing out their faults. Let's look at these two extreme clinical styles so we can understand more clearly how to walk the middle ground. This middle ground is the home of effective confrontation. You must find this middle ground in order to manage denial effectively.

Nondirective Therapy in the Management of Denial

In my experience, nondirective therapy doesn't work very well with clients who are using denial. This is because every time clients start to focus on the painful problems, denial is turned on and they begin thinking and talking about other things in order to turn off the pain. Nondirective therapy methods allow clients to set the agenda of their therapy. The therapist works primarily on issues that the client chooses to focus on. The denial process causes clients to defocus from the painful core issues and to focus instead on secondary issues that don't cause the same level of pain. As a result, nondirective therapy doesn't work very well with clients who are experiencing painful problems protected by strong, automatic, self-reinforcing denial patterns.

A skillful therapist, however, can use guided interviewing techniques to lead clients back to the core problem. But once the client starts thinking and talking about the core problem again, the denial will probably be reactivated. This results in circular manipulative communication that can cause the therapist to feel frustrated, angry, or demoralized. When therapists start feeling this way, they can easily become part of the problem by either using harsh confrontation or giving up and "going with the flow" by allowing the client to be in charge of the agenda of each session.

Here is the paradox: If you don't invite your clients to think about and talk about their painful problems, they won't experience denial, but they also won't be able to resolve the problems that are protected by the denial. If, however, you use directive techniques to get your clients to think and talk about their most painful problems, they will probably use denial to protect themselves from the pain and avoid dealing with the problems. This means that an effective therapist who helps a client to identify and clarify core issues is bound to activate denial in their clients. This also means that effective therapists need to develop skills for managing denial.

Types of Confrontation

One tool in denial management is confrontation. There are two different types of confrontation: a psychonoxious and rational-supportive. **Psychonoxious confrontation** usually makes the denial worse. **Rational-supportive confrontation** helps people work through their denial and recognize, accept, and deal with the truth about what is going wrong in their lives. Let's look at these two types of confrontation in more detail.

Psychonoxious confrontation is based on the belief that harsh, head-to-head confrontations are valuable. Advocates for harsh confrontation believe they must "tear down the wall of denial" and "attack the client's pathological defensive structures." These advocates forget that denial often occurs when their clients are on the verge of being overwhelmed by the pain and problems they are facing. Tearing down their denial without giving them a more effective way of thinking, managing feelings, and solving their problems can cause them to be overwhelmed by their pain and problems. This can make things worse instead of better.

Types of Confrontation

1. Psychonoxious
2. Rational-supportive

I learned the term "psychonoxious confrontation" from Gary Forrest (Forrest, 1982). The term "psychonoxious" is a combination of two roots: *psycho* meaning mind, and *noxious* meaning poisonous. Psychonoxious confrontation is a form of mind-poisonous communication that tends to make people worse instead of better. Here is how you can recognize it when you see it.

Psychonoxious confrontation is permeated with anger and is based on the need to exert power and control over other people. The goal of such confrontation is to attack the client and to get them to submit to the treatment. The mistaken belief underlying the use of psychonoxious confrontation is this: "I must attack, confront, tear down, or destroy the defenses of my clients or my clients will attack, confront, and destroy me. I must control the client or the client will control me."

Psychonoxious confrontation places the emphasis of therapy on forcing clients to change or to comply. The goal is to force clients into doing what is expected rather than teaching them how to make better choices and to develop more effective problem-solving skills.

Psychonoxious confrontation is a power and control tactic. It may make some therapists feel good, but it usually fails to help their clients. Psychonoxious confrontation may be appropriate if you want to brainwash people. It is not appropriate if you want people to learn how to manage their own thinking, feelings, and behavior more effectively. It certainly is not appropriate if you want to teach people how to grow and develop as independent human beings operating according to higher standards of moral and psychological functioning.

Exerting psychological brute force over someone is just one step above exerting physical force. To motivate someone to change through the use of force is a strategy that is very low on a scale of moral development. I firmly believe that violence, whether it be physical or psychological, is the last refuge of the incompetent. When therapists don't know what else to do with clients in hard-core denial, they may resort to psychological violence in the form of harsh psychonoxious confrontation. Let's look at what generally happens when therapists use psychonoxious confrontation.

> When therapists don't know what else to do, they may resort to psychological violence in the form of harsh psychonoxious confrontation.

Fortunately, the human mind is extremely well defended, and it takes more than harsh confrontation to dismantle most people's defensive structures. Rather than stopping denial, harsh psychonoxious confrontation may actually increase the strength and effectiveness of a client's denial. Let's think about the logical consequences of harsh psychonoxious confrontation.

When people are confronted harshly, how can they respond? There appears to be four possibilities: They can: (1) fight back; (2) comply by saying things they don't believe; (3) leave treatment; or (4) become overwhelmed and become dysfunctional.

If they *fight back* against the confrontation they are strengthening their skills at avoidance and absolute denial. They may also be strengthening the antisocial traits that prompt them to challenge authority and to prove they are right at all costs. Clients also learn important lessons about authority figures in general and their therapists in particular. They learn that those in authority are unreasonable people who engage in rigid, head-to-head confrontations for the purpose of gaining power and control.

If they *comply*, clients strengthen their compliance denial pattern and they may also strengthen antisocial traits that prompt them to be convincingly deceitful. Many compliant clients have mastered the skill of quickly finding out what the therapist wants to hear and then saying it.

If they *leave treatment* as a result of harsh confrontation, they are removing themselves from what may be their only source of help and their only chance of facing and solving their problem. Clients who leave treatment as a result of harsh confrontation almost always relapse and end up in worse shape than before.

The clients who become *overwhelmed* by the confrontation usually become dysfunctional. In this case the therapist has actually created more serious problems for a client who already has more problems than they could handle.

When people are harshly confronted they can...

1. Fight back
2. Comply by saying things they don't believe
3. Leave treatment
4. Become overwhelmed and dysfunctional

Therapists who believe in "breaking down" or "tearing down" denial often rationalize the damage in this way: "*We break clients down so we can build them back up as better people.*" Superficially this sounds great. Upon careful examination, however, this approach proves to be antisocial. Someone who tells you their approach to helping you is to tear you down so they can rebuild you from the ground floor up is actually telling you they have little or no respect for who you are as a person. What they usually do is attempt to rebuild people in their image and likeness.

Rational, Directive, Supportive Confrontation

Effective confrontation is rational, directive, and supportive. It is *rational* because the issues being confronted are legitimate and the goal is to discover the truth about what is going on. It is *directive* because it focuses the attention of the client on critical, self-defeating ways of thinking and acting that are causing problems. It is *supportive* because an active listening process is used that supports the core value of the person being confronted while pointing out irrational thinking and self-defeating behavior. Most importantly, effective confrontation *teaches new behaviors* that are more effective than the old self-defeating behaviors at solving the problems.

Effective confrontation separates problems from the person. The problems are the self-defeating ways of thinking and acting being used by clients. The person is the human being who is suffering and in need of help.

Effective confrontation keeps the therapists and clients emotionally connected. When using effective confrontation, therapists do not disconnect by turning their clients into objects or viewing them based on diagnostic or derogatory labels. The goal is to change the self-defeating behavior of their clients and to help them deal with the irrational thought processes that are fueling the denial and the self-defeating behavior.

Effective confrontation gives feedback to clients about their behavior in a way they can understand and accept. The emphasis of effective confrontation is on teaching and learning. The emphasis is not on forcing clients to change. Therapists using healthy confrontation want to help their clients discover the truth about what is wrong and what is needed to effectively deal with it.

> The emphasis of effective confrontation
> is on teaching and learning.
> The emphasis is not on
> forcing clients to change.

Effective confrontation stresses finding the truth. It seeks to discover the reality of both the situation and the total lifestyle context in which the problem developed.

Effective confrontation occurs in a context of collaboration, trust, and mutual concern. Collaboration means that two people work together in harmony to achieve shared goals. To collaborate effectively, therapists must establish effective relationships with their clients before engaging in confrontation. The therapeutic relationship is used to direct or focus the attention of clients on important issues they are trying to avoid, deny, or minimize.

Effective confrontation is one ingredient in the therapist's clinical approach. It is integrated within the context of other therapeutic methods or techniques. In other words, therapists using effective confrontation do not set out with the goal of confronting denial. They set out to identify and clarify the client's problems and to develop a problem-solving strategy. The denial emerged in the context of problem identification or problem solving. The therapist then used effective confrontation within the context of the overall direction of the therapy.

The goal of effective confrontation is to build clients up, not to tear them down. When therapists "tear down denial" they may be taking away the only survival tool their clients have. The goal of effective confrontation is not to tear down denial. The goal is to expose the denial, show that it is not working, and then to give new tools for dealing with the anger, fear, pain, guilt, and shame that will emerge when they stop denying the problem.

Effective confrontation clearly exposes patterns of denial and defensiveness so they can be openly and directly explored. By exploring them, clients can see why those patterns are counterproductive or self-defeating. Then they can choose to stop using denial and to make a commitment to refocus on the therapeutic process that activated the denial in the first place.

Effective confrontation puts clients in a position where they need to reinterpret their previous views and beliefs in the light of new experience and information. This must be done in a way that allows this new view to become integrated into their belief system. The new beliefs must set the stage for immediate behavioral change and the slow, gradual, and consistent change or evolution of the level of moral functioning and the personality style of the client. The goal of effective confrontation is not just to force clients to change their behavior. The goal is to help clients improve their character and positively transform their personalities.

The Collaborative Model of Denial Management

Effective denial management requires a collaborative model that invites clients to become part of the process of identifying and solving their problems. To be collaborative it is important to recognize that the problem is not between the client and the therapist. The problem is between the client and the client. One therapist who completed the training in the denial management process put it this way: *"Before the training I would take it personally when clients tried to use denial. I thought the denial was directed at me. Once I learned that denial had nothing to do with me, it became easier to detach and help the client focus on the inner conflicts that were being projected onto me."*

My recommendation is this: Don't try to attack denial. Instead, become genuinely concerned about working with your clients to find out what is wrong and what can be done to deal with it effectively. Managing denial in a collaborative way is much more effective than trying to manage it from an adversarial position. The difficulty is getting the client to collaborate. Here's why.

Recommendation

- Don't try to attack denial.
- Do become genuinely concerned about working with the client to find out what is wrong and what can be done to deal with it.

Each denial pattern contains within it an invitation for the therapist to become part of the problem by fighting with the client. **The first step in building a collaboration is to refuse to accept the invitation to fight.** The best way not to fight is to have no preconceived notions about what is wrong with the client, and to have the primary goal of working collaboratively with the client to figure what is wrong and how to best deal with what is wrong.

The problem is that clients who are in the habit of using hard-core denial are very good at inviting people to become part of their problem. Once you accept the invitation, you will be drawn into a series of transactions that pull you off center and take away your control of the clinical process. In essence, clients in denial use elaborate unconscious strategies to control the clinical process. Once they are in charge, the assessment and treatment process is condemned to fail.

The solution is to recognize denial, refuse the client's invitation to become part of their problem, and then focus on identifying and solving the core problems that are hidden by denial. The process is called feeling management, and here's how it works.

Feeling Management and Denial

Denial can be managed by learning how to deal effectively with the painful feelings that are turned on when thinking about or talking about the problem. This is because denial is driven by intense feelings of pain, shame, guilt, anger, and fear. The more skilled a person is at managing those feelings, the easier it will be for your clients to "work through" denial and face the real problem.

Feelings can be effectively managed by a four-step process: First we recognize that we are having a feeling by noticing or self-monitoring the rise and fall of our inner experiences. When we recognize a strong inner experience we consciously say to ourselves, "I'm feeling something!" and then we ask the question, "What am I feeling?" This focuses our attention on the inner experience and allows us to notice what is going on. If you are working with someone who is using strong denial, it is a good idea to quickly assess their ability to sit still and notice their inner experiences. If they can't, some form of inner awareness or sensitivity training exercises might be needed.

The second step in managing a feeling is to name it. The better our emotional vocabulary, the more effective we will be at recognizing and managing feelings. This means that it is usually a good idea to check out the client's ability to explain their feelings and inner experiences with words. If clients don't have words to describe their feelings, we need to give them new words and help them expand their emotional vocabulary. I call this process "building an emotional vocabulary."

The third step is to communicate the feeling to someone who will listen to us, understand us, and take us seriously. This communication to another sensitive, caring person leads to the fourth step of integrating the feeling.

The Feeling Management Process

1. Recognize when we start to have a feeling.
2. Name the feeling.
3. Talk about the feeling.
4. Integrate the feeling.

Remember that the key feelings driving denial are pain, shame, guilt, anger, and fear. The antidote to those feelings is a sense of detached peacefulness that is often called "being centered." It is not enough to teach clients how to recognize and label the emotional drivers of denial. We need to teach them to recognize and activate the feelings of detached peacefulness.

In other words, we need to use immediate here-and-now relaxation training to teach clients in denial how to lower their stress levels and get centered. From this centered state of mind, clients can begin exploring and labeling their feelings and emotions. Unfortunately, there is a major obstacle to learning how to get centered. That obstacle is denial.

Triggers of Denial in Substance Abusers

There are specific triggers of denial in people who abuse or are dependent on alcohol or other drugs. Their denial will be activated whenever they are asked to think about or talk about their alcohol or drug use or the problems caused by their drinking or drugging.

Triggers of Denial in Substance Abuse

Denial is activated in substance abusers whenever you get them to think or talk about...

1. their alcohol and drug use;
2. problems caused by their alcohol and drug use.

This means that therapists need to be prepared to use denial management methods when they directly ask their clients about their alcohol or drug use or related problems.

The activation of denial in response to questions about drinking and drug use can be a diagnostic indicator of a substance use disorder. If you ask about drinking or drugging and the person responds with no denial, the odds are they either don't have a problem, are in recovery, or have had so much previous treatment that they have learned how to play the therapy game. Usually, denial in response to questions about alcohol and drug use means the person has a problem.

There were two men, one an alcoholic and one a social drinker, who worked in the same building and went out for lunch together. They both had a beer with lunch, came back into the office building and got on a crowded elevator to go back to their offices on the top floor. Halfway up a coworker turned to the social drinker and asked, *"Have you been drinking?"* Without any hesitation or emotional reaction, the social drinker responded, *"Yes, I had a beer with my pizza. Why do you ask?"* This coworker never asked the alcoholic if he had been drinking. Why? Because the alcoholic held his breath for twelve floors so no one could smell alcohol on his breath.

Methods for Building Trust

One of the most important goals of denial management is to help the client trust the therapist. Denial management is a trust-building method based on an open and honest pursuit of the truth. For this to happen clients must respect and trust the therapist. This means therapists must genuinely attempt to listen to and understand what their client is saying. They must also take their clients seriously and affirm them and their right to their opinions. This is called genuineness. The therapist must genuinely support the client as a human being and have empathy for the client's position.

Empathy is only possible if therapists remember that people using hard-core denial are on the verge of being overwhelmed and destroyed by what, on some level, they perceive to be overwhelming problems causing unbearable emotional pain. The therapist using effective confrontation needs to be able to see beyond the denial and to sense the client's core pain and frustration. They must be able to stay connected with the reality that clients use denial as a survival strategy. At times their denial may be their only available survival tool.

For Confrontation to Be Effective Clients Must Feel:

1. Listened to
2. Understood
3. Taken Seriously
4. Affirmed as People

Here are some guidelines you can use to help your clients trust you:

1. Follow a consistent format and set of rules in your therapy sessions. In this way your clients can learn to trust the process. Your clients learn how to participate successfully in the therapy process. They learn the skills needed to work effectively in therapy and develop trust in the process because they know they will not get unpleasant surprises.

2. Have a plan and stay focused. This means learning a system that allows you to explore the client's problems in an orderly fashion. It also means having a standard approach to problem solving or problem resolution. This way the therapy can shift to a collaborative skill-building activity. The therapist's job can then become involved in teaching clients how to develop the skills of introspection, self-assessment, and problem solving.

3. Find something about the client that you can like, respect, or admire. This will allow you to be able to genuinely support the human being who is sitting before you. This also sets the stage for building on the core strengths you have found and allows you to shift fluidly from pointing out self-defeating tendencies to supporting the client in building on positive skills or attributes they already possess.

4. Remember, your goal is to show the client a new and more helpful interpretation of reality. Your clients can trust you only when they see your goal is to help them find new, more effective ways in thinking about and dealing with their problems. To do this you must help your clients present their current understanding of what is going on in their life and then help them reinterpret that understanding in more helpful ways.

Systems for Denial Management

1. **Denial Management Interactional Process**
   • A communication system for use in group and individual sessions when denial is activated
2. **Denial Management Exercises**
   • Exercises that teach people to understand, recognize, and manage their own denial
3. **Denial Self-Management Training**
   • A psychoeducation process that uses the denial management exercises in a classroom setting

---

5. Learn and use effective systems for managing denial. There are effective methods for managing denial. You can learn about these systems, integrate them into your clinical style, and improve your effectiveness with clients in denial. There are three basic denial management systems that can work together in managing clients exhibiting strong denial and treatment resistance. These are: (1) *The Denial Management Interactional Process*, which is a communication system that can be used in group and individual sessions whenever denial is activated. (2) *The Denial Management Clinical Exercises*, which are a series of nine structured exercises that can be used in group and individual sessions to guide clients through a systematic process of understanding, recognizing, and managing their own denial. (3) *Denial Self-Management Training (DSMT),* which is a structured psychoeducation process that teaches people how to identify and manage their own denial. Let's look at these three models in more detail.

2–3: Denial Management Counseling—The Interactional Process

The Denial Management Interactional Process is a structured communication process for recognizing and effectively managing denial as it comes up in individual or group sessions. It can be used in both individual and group therapy sessions when denial is activated. It consists of a seven-step procedure for clinical communication that is divided into two preparation steps and five intervention steps.

The *preparation steps* are: (1) Asking a sequence of focusing questions and (2) processing all answers with active listening. The *intervention steps* are: (3) Identifying denial when it occurs; (4) exposing denial when it interferes with problem solving; (5) educating about denial; (6) challenging denial; and (7) teaching denial self-management.

The Denial Management Interactional Process

The Preparation Steps

1. **Ask a Sequence of Focusing Questions**
   - Focus on the target problem.
2. **Process All Answers with Active Listening**
   - Make clients feel listened to, understood, taken seriously, and affirmed.

The Intervention Steps

3. **Identify Denial**
   - Recognize when denial is turned on.
4. **Expose Denial**
   - Point out the denial pattern to the client and talk about it openly.
5. **Educate about Denial**
   - Explain the denial pattern.
6. **Challenge Denial**
   - Give permission to deal directly with core problems.
   - Give injunctions against continued denial.
7. **Teach Denial Self-Management**
   - Show how to stop denial and directly solve problems.

The first two steps—asking a sequence of focusing questions and processing the answers using active listening—invite clients to think and talk about their problems without activating severe denial. These first two steps are critical to effective denial management and are often called the *preparation steps of denial management.*

These steps are not only important in managing denial, they are an essential part of good clinical counseling skills. Asking a sequence of focusing questions and using active listening to process the answers should be used with all clients before denial becomes a problem. If this is done, therapists are more likely to establish a collaborative relationship with their clients and prevent denial and resistance from occurring. These first two steps will also allow therapists to manage mild denial before it escalates and sabotages the treatment process. If severe denial is activated, these steps will have created a solid foundation for managing it.

Goals of the Preparation Steps of The Denial Management Interactional Process

- To establish a collaborative relationship with the client
- To prevent denial from occurring whenever possible
- To effectively manage mild denial and prevent escalation into severe denial whenever possible
- To create a solid foundation for managing severe denial should it occur

---

Notice that a special denial management treatment plan is used only when denial is so strong and persistent that it prevents clients from completing the action steps of their treatment plan. The primary goal of the last five steps of the Denial Management Process (steps 3–7) is to manage severe and persistent denial should it occur. This is done by changing the focus of the therapy from directly solving the target problems to identifying and managing the denial that is sabotaging the problem-solving process.

Goals of the Intervention Steps of The Denial Management Interactional Process

- To manage severe and persistent denial should it occur
- By refocusing from direct problem solving to identifying and managing denial

---

First, let's look at the preparation steps (steps 1–2) of the denial management interactional process in detail. Then we will explore the intervention steps (steps 3–7).

Step 1: Ask a Sequence of Focusing Questions

The first step in denial management is to ask a sequence of *focusing questions*. A focusing question is an inquiry that asks clients to think and talk about their target problems. It is important to individualize the questions to focus on the unique problems of each client. A *structured clinical interview* can be developed by preparing a sequence of related focusing questions that invites clients to explore their target problems in progressively more detail and look for related problems.

The best focusing questions are open-ended questions that cannot be answered with a yes or a no. A good *initial opening question* for a first interview is, "What caused you to come to counseling at this time?" In answering this question clients are forced to reveal themselves and project their attitudes and beliefs.

Closed questions, those that can be answered with a yes or a no, generally make poor focusing questions because they don't give you much information. Think of starting a session with the question, "Were you referred here by the court?" The client answers "yes." Now the therapist must play twenty questions to try and find all of the pieces of the puzzle.

Using clear focusing questions is essential in teaching clients how to identify and manage denial. These questions get clients to think and talk about the target problems that brought them into treatment. The best focusing questions move from general problems to progressively more detailed descriptions of the problems.

Here is a simple sequence of focusing questions that can be used when you suspect a substance-use problem.

1. "What caused you to come into counseling at this time?"

2. "What are the three or four most important or most serious problems that are going on in your life right now?"

3. "How are each of those problems related to your use of alcohol or drugs?"

4. "What do you think will happen to each of those problems if you keep using alcohol or drugs?" ("What's the best thing that could happen? What's the worst that could happen? What's the most likely thing that could happen?")

5. "Given the potential consequences of alcohol and drug use, do you think it's a good idea to keep using alcohol or drugs at this time?" (If yes, ask "why." If no, ask "why not.")

6. "Are you willing to make a decision to stop using alcohol or drugs for the duration of our counseling together?" (If yes, ask "why." If no, ask "why not." If unsure, ask "Explain your dilemma."

By reviewing this sequence of questions the session plan becomes obvious. The questions are designed to go somewhere. They are designed to produce an outcome. That outcome is to invite clients to think and talk about their most important problems. If the focusing questions are designed properly, clients will have only two choices: face their problems honestly or use denial to avoid facing their problems.

Well-designed focusing questions give the client two choices:

1. face their problems honestly or
2. use denial to avoid facing their problems.

Let's use the same six questions, but focus them on exploring the relationship of a controlling personality style to the presenting problems. I call clients with controlling personalities *Top Dog Personality Styles*. They tend to show a combination of symptoms from the DSM Cluster B Personality Styles. They tend to be *antisocial* (they challenge authority, break rules, and victimize others); *narcissistic* (they are self-centered and tend to diminish the importance of other people); *histrionic* (they want to be the center of attention and need dramatic problems to talk about to keep them center stage); *borderline* (they can have radical shifts in self-concept from an exaggerated sense of self-worth—"I am God" to an exaggerated sense of low self-esteem—"I am nothing."

Here is how the six focusing questions can be modified to look at the relationship between the clients presenting problems and their top dog personality style:

1. "What caused you to come into counseling at this time?"

2. "What are the three or four most important or most serious problems that are going on in your life right now?"

3. "How are each of those problems related to your tendency to want to put yourself in a one-up position and to put others in a one-down position?"

4. "What do you think will happen to each of those problems if you keep insisting on putting yourself in a one-up position and putting others in a one-down position?" ("What's the best that could happen? What's the worst that could happen? What's the most likely thing that could happen?")

5. "Given the potential consequences, do you think it's a good idea to keep putting yourself in a one-up position and to putting others in a one-down position?" (If yes, ask "why." If no, ask "why not.")

6. "Are you willing to make a decision to stop insisting upon putting yourself in a one-up position and to putting others in a one-down position for the duration of our counseling together?" (If yes, ask "why?" If no, ask "why not." If unsure, ask "Explain your dilemma."

This sequence of six focusing questions is clear and straightforward. They can be rewritten to focus on any core problem area. Clients who are not in strong denial will be able to answer these questions directly with a little bit of guidance and direction from the therapist. Clients in strong denial, however, will have difficulty directly answering the questions without using denial to sidetrack the session and avoid answering the questions. Here is a brief transcript of a typical session with a client who is in strong denial.

Therapist: What caused you to come to counseling at this time?

Client: I don't know?

Therapist: You're saying you don't know what caused you to come into counseling? Is that correct?

Client: That's right.

Therapist: Excuse me, but I'm confused. Are you telling me you have absolutely no idea what caused you to come to this counseling session? Am I hearing you correctly?

Client: Well, I guess the judge sent me.

Therapist: You guess the judge sent you. *<Pause>* Are you saying that you're not sure if the judge sent you or not?

Client: Alright! The judge sent me, but it's all a big mistake. I shouldn't have to be here.

Therapist: So you're saying the judge did send you, but you think it was a mistake, and you think you shouldn't have to be here. Is that correct?

Client: Yes.

Therapist: Could you tell me more about that?

Notice that at this point in the interview we are not even close to getting a complete answer to the first question. This is a clear indicator that the client is using denial to keep from thinking and talking about the real problem.

Step 2: Process All Answers with Active Listening

It is important to listen carefully and to respond genuinely to what your clients are saying. In the above interview, the therapist was using an active listening process. The careful use of active listening is essential in managing denial.

Researcher Stephen Glenn reviewed clinical research from NIDA drug prevention programs in the 1970s. He was interested in discovering what factors were important in motivating adolescent substance abusers to come back for a second outpatient session. He found four subjective experiences that are highly predictive of whether or not a client will return for a second session. The clients who felt listened to, understood, taken seriously, and affirmed as people tended to come back. Clients who tended not to come back generally felt they were not listened to, were misunderstood, were not taken seriously, or were not affirmed as people.

So the question is, "How do we set the stage in our group and individual sessions for people to feel listened to, understood, taken seriously, and affirmed?" The answer is to use a systematic *active* listening process.

Let's review the steps of the active listening procedure and then look at how active listening can be specifically applied to the management of denial and resistance.

Active listening is used at every step of the denial management process. The active listening process consists of seven steps.

Active Listening

1. Ask a Question
2. Listen to the Answer
3. Give Same Word Feedback
4. Do an Accuracy Check
5. Use Other Word Feedback (Paraphrasing)
6. Do an Accuracy Check
7. Go on to the Next Question

1. **Ask a Question:** Ask a specific open-ended question that focuses the client's attention on the specific issue you want to process. (*Open-ended questions* cannot be answered with a "yes" or a "no." *Closed questions* can be answered with a "yes" or a "no." *Focus questions* force a client to choose between a limited number of choices, usually two.)

2. **Listen to the Answer:** Hear what your clients are saying. Try to understand the answer from their point of view. Don't project your point of view onto your clients. When therapists project their point of view onto their clients, I call it *leaving footprints.* We leave footprints when we have a preconceived notion or belief about the client and then use leading questions or suggestions to invite the client to buy into that belief.

A clear question that does not leave footprints would be, "Have you ever been in treatment for a substance use problem before?" A loaded question that is virtually guaranteed to leave footprints is, "You have been in treatment for substance abuse problems before, haven't you?"

The most difficult part of active listening is to suspend your preconceived ideas about your clients and to really hear and reflect back what they are saying. Unless you can listen and truly hear your clients, you won't be able to complete the rest of the process.

3. **Give Same Word Feedback:** Tell clients what you heard them say using the exact same words they used. A good way to do this is to say something like this: "What I heard you say is *<use the exact words of the client>*."

For same-word feedback to work the therapist must integrate it into their clinical style so the communication is *genuine.* If same-word feedback is used as a sterile, canned process it will turn clients off. It can, however, be an effective communication tool if therapists use it to genuinely communicate, both verbally and nonverbally, that they are interested and want to understand what their clients are saying. Using same-word feedback is what makes the client feel listened to and understood. They feel like you are taking them seriously and affirming them when you consistently do accuracy checks.

4. **Do an Accuracy Check:** After using same-word feedback ask the client if you heard them correctly. You can say something like, "Did I get it right?" If the client says no, then you can say, "I'm sorry. What you're saying is really important to me and I want to hear you correctly. Could you tell me again?" This process is called an *accuracy check.*

When you do accuracy checks there are several rules:

(1)   *Don't get defensive.* If the client says that you didn't understand them correctly take it in stride, apologize for the misunderstanding, and ask them to repeat what they said. If you get defensive, you have accepted an invitation to enter your client's denial structure, and by doing so you will become part of the client's problem instead of part of the solution.

(2) *Don't confront.* The goal of an accuracy check is to make sure you are understanding the client. It is not a time for you to point out or confront irrational thinking, provocative nonverbal messages, or inconsistencies with previous answers. There will be time for that later.

(3) *Stay calm and centered.* One of the signals a therapist can use to sense when they are being drawn into their client's denial is to suddenly be drawn off center and experience strong feelings that cause you to react instead of respond. One of the goals of denial is to get therapists upset so they will become reactive, defensive, and start using emotional reasoning instead of good clinical judgment. Once therapists start reacting emotionally instead of responding professionally to their clients, they have shifted the control of the session from therapist to client. Therapists can avoid doing this by staying calm, centered, and recognizing any surge of strong emotion as a warning sign that the client may be inviting them to participate in their denial.

(4) *Accept responsibility for not hearing correctly even if you did hear correctly.* The goal of doing an accuracy check is not to be right. The goal is to make sure you are understanding your clients and that your clients can see that you are making a genuine effort to see the problem from their point of view. As a result, if the client said you didn't hear them correctly, accept responsibility, restate your desire to understand, and ask them to explain it again. In this way you can step out of the power struggle and get the client to look at what they are really thinking and saying.

Many times clients answer questions using *automatic irrational thinking*. When these clients hear the therapist repeat exactly what they said, many of these clients can hear the irrationality behind what they are saying. This phenomenon is called re-perception. When we think a thought privately in our own mind, we perceive it at one level of consciousness. When we are forced to put our private thought into words, we perceive it at a second level of consciousness. When we hear someone repeat back what we have said, we perceive it at a third and more objective state of consciousness. Writing it down and confronting the idea in black and white produces even more distance and objectivity in reviewing the thought or idea.

When clients hear exactly what they are saying and recognize the inherent irrationality of their statement, they will often blame the therapist for misunderstanding rather than accept responsibility for giving an irrational answer. If therapists accept the responsibility for not hearing correctly and ask the client to "tell me again," many clients will develop a more accurate and rational answer the second time around and be able to save face in the process. Remember, the goal is not for therapists to prove how right or smart they are. The goal is for clients to learn to face and cope with the truth.

Re-perception is the process of becoming fully conscious of our thoughts by

1. Thinking privately in our own mind;
2. Putting our private thought into words;
3. Hearing what we said repeated back to us; and
4. Writing it down and seeing the idea in black and white.

---

5. **Use Different Word Feedback (Paraphrasing):** Once clients have accepted your same-word feedback as accurate, it is time to begin moving them into your frame of reference. This is done by translating what they said into different words that force them to look at the problem from a different point of view. This process is called *paraphrasing* and it is different from same-word feedback.

When you paraphrase you take your best understanding of the meaning of what the client is saying and translate that meaning into different words. Because you are changing the words, it is possible that your clients won't agree with your interpretation. Your interpretation could also trigger or activate denial. As a result, whenever you use paraphrasing it is a good idea to "buy insurance" so that if you get it wrong, or if the client gets upset with what you said, you will have a way to deal with it effectively.

A good way to buy insurance is to say something like this: *"I think I understand you, but I want to be sure. Let me tell you what I'm hearing you say in my own words. Then you tell me if I got it right. What I'm hearing you say is* tell the client what you heard using other words."

Paraphrasing is done to *clarify, challenge,* or *redirect* the client's thinking. Whenever you use paraphrasing you will, to some degree or another, leave footprints in the client's consciousness. This is because one of the purposes of paraphrasing is to give clients new words, ideas, and concepts for understanding their problems. The goal is to get clients to look at their problems from a different point of view so they can see aspects of those problem they didn't notice before.

> One of the purposes of paraphrasing is
> to give clients new words, ideas, and concepts
> for understanding their problems.

It is during this fifth step of active listening that we can use a number of special techniques to directly deal with denial. We will show you exactly how to do that later. For now, let's complete the description of the basic active listening process.

6. **Do an Accuracy Check:** Whenever you use paraphrasing it is important to do an accuracy check. Ask the client if you heard them correctly. Watch for nonverbal signs of disagreement. Many clients will comply and say yes when they don't really think you got it right. If they say you heard them wrong, apologize and ask them to explain it to you again.

Watch for nonverbal signals that the client doesn't really think you fully understood. If your gut tells you your paraphrasing didn't really connect with the client, ask them how accurate they think your statement is. You can say something like this: *"Let's score how accurate you think my feedback is from your point of view. A ten means I got it 100 percent right. A zero means I totally missed the mark. What do you think? How well did I understand what you were saying?"*

This approach gives clients permission to think critically and to give you critical feedback. It also starts training them in how to use ten-point rating scales to improve the accuracy of communication and measure progress.

7. **Go On to the Next Question:** Once you've gotten an answer to your question, move to the next question in your sequence of focusing questions. Remember, the goal of the client's denial is to get you to abandon your original plan and follow the client's agenda, which will usually lead you away

from the core or central problem that is protected by denial. There are two problems to guard against: (1) Moving on before getting a complete answer to the question; and (2) beating a question to death by probing for unnecessary details. It is important to get a clear, concrete answer to the question and then move on. There are two techniques that are especially helpful in getting complete answers without beating a question to death. These are:

1. **Visualizing the Answer:** You can use a visualization technique to judge whether a question has been completely answered. Try to visualize the answer to the question in order to get a complete picture of the situation in your mind. If you can see a complete picture, and that picture makes sense in the context of the session, you probably have a complete answer and can move on. If, however, the picture is incomplete or fuzzy, it is important to probe for more details until a clear picture forms in your mind.

2. **Using Standard Clarifying Questions:** There are six clarifying questions you can use to probe for more details: I call them the *Who, What, When, Where, Why, and How Questions.* "Who was there? What were they doing? What were you doing? When did this happen—year, month, day, time? Where were you when it happened? Why did you think it happened like it did? How did it occur?"

When talking with clients in denial it is important to invite them to tell you about the issues in concrete and specific terms. You want them to tell you about concrete details of incidents that occurred at a particular time. You want to avoid settling for vague general accounts about what "always" or "usually" happens. Ask your clients to identify by name the people involved. Don't accept vague identifiers like "them" or "other people." Get curious about the concrete facts rather than judgments, opinions, and graphic metaphors.

When a client says, *"The judge blew me away!"* ask, "*What exactly did the judge do or say that blew you away?*"

Common Problems with Active Listening: There are two other problems that commonly interfere with the active listening process: The One-Or Two-Word Answer and the Big Dump.

The One-Word Answer: Some clients will respond to a focusing question with a word or a short phrase. You might ask, *"Why are you here?"* The client says, *"The judge."* When something like this happens use same-word feedback. Be sure to repeat the exact same words the client used. In the above example I would say, *"The judge sent you. Is that correct?"*

The client will probably respond by saying something like, "Yes!" Then you can say, *"I don't understand. Can you tell me more about that?"*

Here's another example:

Therapist: Why are you here?

Client: I screwed up!

Therapist: You're saying you screwed up. Is that correct?

Client: Yeah!

Therapist: I don't understand. Tell me more about how you screwed up.

The Big Dump (The Very Long Answer): Some clients will respond to a focusing question with a very long answer I call the Big Dump. This often happens when clients have intense feelings and have not had the opportunity to vent those feelings with anyone. They get started and just keep going. When this happens the therapist literally gets left out of the process as the client shifts from a dialogue with the therapist to a dramatic monologue with the therapist acting as a private audience.

One way to manage a big dump is to let the client go through the entire answer without an interruption. If you interrupt, the client tends to get angry and annoyed. The interruption increases their commitment to finish saying what they want to say. Your attempt to stop them creates a conflict. If you let them vent without interruption, most clients run out of steam within a few minutes. When they stop, say something like, *"Wow, that's a lot of information. I really want to understand what you're telling me, but to be quite honest, you said more than I could understand. Could we go back to the beginning and review what you said point by point?"*

Then start at the beginning and ask specific focusing questions that lead the client point by point through the major points of what they said. What often happens is that the client will be unable to repeat most of what came out during the big dump. This is why it's important to have a pencil and paper in front of you during sessions. When your clients move into a big dump, you can jot down a sequence of bullet points that will help recreate the sequence of ideas that are spilling out. The big dump is often full of automatic and unconscious self-talk statements that the client is only vaguely aware of and that they immediately forget. This is why it is so crucial to slowly and carefully review the information in detail.

The Activation of Denial when Using Active Listening: Denial is a common problem that many therapists experience when trying to do active listening. This is because the active listening process, when done properly, begins to focus the client on thinking and talking about the core problems that are protected by denial or a defense system.

This is why the process of giving same-word feedback and paraphrasing what clients are telling you can increase stress and trigger intense emotions. *Same-word feedback* forces clients to hear what they are saying to the therapist. *Paraphrasing* forces them to reflect on the possible underlying meaning of the things they are saying.

Both processes put the client in the position of hearing and needing to consciously respond to thoughts and ideas that had previously been private, unconscious, and automatic. Both processes force clients to think and talk about the core issues and asks them to expose their automatic thinking processes. Because actively listening will generally activate a denial process, let's review a simple list of do's and don'ts that can help you to more effectively manage the denial if it is activated (see page 102).

A Summary of the Active Listening Process: In summary, the active listening process is a structured communication process that is used in all steps of dealing with denial. The active listening process consists of seven steps: (1) Ask a Question, (2) Listen to the Answer, (3) Give Same-Word Feedback (What I heard you say is), (4) Do an Accuracy Check ("Did I hear you correctly?"), (5) Use Paraphrasing ("I want to be sure that I heard you correctly. Let me put what I heard you say into different words and you tell me if I got it right."), (6) Accuracy Check ("Did I hear you correctly?"), (7) Ask the next question.

Many times the active listening process alone will be sufficient to interrupt the denial process. If the denial is severe and persistent, Step 5 the paraphrasing step of actively listening can be modified to give a powerful tool for dealing directly with denial. Let's explore in-depth how active listening can be specifically used to deal directly with denial.

If Denial Is Activated...

Do .... 1. Recognize that the client is using denial.
2. Step out of the power struggle.
3. Apologize for misunderstanding.
4. Tell the client you are interested in hearing what they said.
5. Ask the client to explain what they really meant.

Don't .... 1. Ignore the denial and pretend that nothing is happening.
2. Try to prove you are right.
3. Blame the client for saying it wrong.
4. Give the impression you are angry or annoyed.
5. Keep going as if nothing had happened.

When to Use the Denial Management Process Intervention Steps (steps 3–7): Having a well-developed sequence of focusing questions (Step 1) and using an effective active listening process (Step 2) can either prevent denial from occurring or effectively manage mild denial when it occurs without disrupting the implementation of the treatment plan.

For many clients, however, denial has become a way of life. These clients have integrated denial patterns into their basic habitual behavior and have accepted the mistaken beliefs that underlie denial as a basic truth of life. To manage denial in these clients requires more than focusing questions and active listening. The therapist must understand the dynamics of denial, recognize it when it occurs, understand the basic principles of denial management, and intervene by applying those basic principles to the specific denial patterns that the client is using.

The Intervention Steps of the Denial Management Interactional Process should be used whenever denial is so severe and persistent that it interferes with the active listening process, prevents the therapist from completing a basic series of focusing questions, or prevents the client from completing important recovery tasks. When the last five steps of DMP directly intervene on and manage specific denial patterns they are called the DMP I.

First, I will summarize how the last five steps of the Denial Management Interactional Process work together, in sequence, to interrupt denial and refocus on the target problem. Then I will review each of the last five steps of DMP in greater detail.

As we discussed, denial is exposed by involving the client in an active listening process. Use the first four steps of active listening (ask a question, listen to the answer, give same-word feedback, and do an accuracy check) until you have managed to achieve some level of rapport with the client. Then, when you are ready to begin reframing or redirecting the client's thinking by using a paraphrasing process, use the sequence of five paraphrasing steps (the intervention steps of the Denial Management Interactional Process) that are designed to deal directly with denial:

(1) **Identify Denial:** Identify that the client is using denial by the behavioral goal of the denial pattern by listening to your gut, looking for nonverbal indicators, identifying the behavioral goal, identifying the cognitive theme and related self-talk, and identifying the mistaken beliefs.

(2) **Expose the Denial:** Expose the denial pattern so clients can see what they are doing.

(3) **Educate about Denial:** Educate about the denial pattern so clients can understand why the denial pattern won't work.

(4) **Challenge the Denial:** Challenge the denial pattern by giving a therapeutic injunction against continued use of denial and therapeutic permission to look honestly at the core problem.

(5) **Teach Denial Self-Management:** Show clients new ways of thinking and acting so they can recognize their denial when it is activated and stop their own denial when it starts to interfere with their recovery.

Let's look at each of these five denial intervention steps in more detail.

Step 3: Identifying Denial When It Occurs

Identifying Denial When It Occurs

1. Listen to Your Gut
2. Look for Nonverbal Indicators
3. Identify the Behavioral Goal
4. Identify the Cognitive Theme and Related Self-Talk
5. Identify the Mistaken Beliefs

Before you can manage severe denial you must recognize that the client is using it. This may sound like a self-evident fact, but in actual clinical practice it can be difficult to distinguish genuine therapeutic communication from denial. The identification process is improved by studying the various denial patterns and learning to recognize the behavioral goal, cognitive theme and self-talk, and mistaken beliefs associated with each denial pattern.

So Step 3 of the Denial Management Interactional Process is to *identify when the client is using denial.* In other words, you need to recognize that the client has shifted from genuine communication to the use of a denial pattern. The best way to do this is to listen to your gut, look for nonverbal indicators, and identify the behavioral goal, related self-talk (cognitive theme), and mistaken beliefs.

1. **Listen to Your Gut:** First you "listen to your gut." You will feel the difference between genuine communication and de-

nial. You may not know exactly what is wrong, but you will sense that something has shifted. The more clinical experience you have, the better your intuition will be trained to pick up the shift from genuine communication to denial. If your gut tells you something has changed, it probably has. If your gut tells you the client is not being honest or genuine, they probably aren't. If your gut says you are being conned or manipulated, you probably are. Trust your gut and your professionally trained intuition. But don't act exclusively on your gut reaction. Our intuitive senses can be and often are incorrect, but they should always be honored as a message that we need to go to the next step.

2. **Look for Nonverbal Indicators:** When the client moves from genuine communication into denial something will change about the client. These changes are often seen in the type of eye contact, the expression on their face, their posture in the chair, or their level of tension. Whenever your gut says something is wrong, *consciously look for the nonverbal indicators* of denial in the client.

The client will either become a *hot responder* and begin overreacting to things that are said or they will become a *cold responder* and detach and become dead and distant in their responses.

3. **Identify the Behavioral Goal:** When your gut says that something's wrong and you observe the nonverbal signs of the shift from genuine communication to a hot or cold response, it's time to consciously identify the goal of the client's behavior.

Alfred Adler has suggested that all human behavior is goal oriented. In other words, people do things in order to accomplish something or to get a payoff. Their behavior also invites others to either move with them or move against them in achieving the goal. This means that clients will give therapists invitations to join with them in their denial. Clients will invite their therapists to become part of the problem instead of part of the solution.

The therapists who accept this invitation usually become enablers to their clients' addiction and to the other mental and emotional problems the client is facing. In my early mental health training we called this *supporting the client's pathology.* In my early addiction training we called this *enabling.*

The point is that denial patterns are goal-oriented behaviors. Each denial pattern has a behavioral goal that is similar to, yet slightly different from the others. It is important to recognize the behavioral goal of a denial pattern because in order to teach the client how to recognize and manage it, you must show the client how to achieve the goal of denial in a more healthy and self-enhancing way.

> Teaching clients how to recognize and manage denial means showing them how to deal with their problems in a more effective way.

All denial patterns share a common behavioral goal: to manage a painful problem by refusing to honestly think or talk about. Each distinct denial pattern, however, has a unique goal or behavioral method by which the client avoids thinking about or talking about the core problem. It is important to understand the general behavioral goals of denial and then to understand the specific means whereby each specific denial pattern seeks to accomplish the goal.

4. **Identify the Cognitive Theme and Related Self-Talk:** Cognitive therapists have suggested that it is helpful to teach clients how to identify and consciously manage the self-talk patterns or the silent conversations they have in their minds. Each denial pattern is distinguished by a self-talk conversation that is built around a specific cognitive theme. Once the cognitive theme is identified, a number of standard cognitive therapy procedures can be used to help the client identify, clarify, and change the self-talk patterns that are preventing them from seeing the truth about what is wrong and what they need to do to correct it. So once you have identified the behavioral goal, it is helpful to ask yourself what type of self-talk could be causing the client to pursue that goal.

Avoidance, for example, has the theme, "I'll talk about anything but the real problem!" and is accompanied by self-talk statements that change the subject and steer the therapist away from the issue without directly denying or refusing to talk about the issue. Absolute denial has a different behavioral goal: "I'll prove that I don't have a problem!" It is often accompanied by self-talk that says, "No not me, I don't have a problem."

5. **Identify the Mistaken Beliefs:** Each denial pattern and the related self-talk patterns are built on a set of underlying mistaken beliefs or false assumptions about what is true and what is not true. These mistaken beliefs represent the client's personal truth. It is the truth as the client sees it at the moment. The client assumes these underlying beliefs are true. The client is usually unaware of these underlying beliefs and has accepted them uncritically.

> Exposing and Challenging the Mistaken Beliefs
> that Drive Denial Cause the Denial to
> Lose Its Power

The problem is that this "truth as the client sees it" is often based on a belief without evidence. Once the belief is exposed, you can challenge the belief by pointing out that there is no valid evidence that supports the truthfulness of the belief. Once these beliefs are exposed and challenged they tend to lose their power and the client no longer gains psychological benefit from using them. There are standard cognitive therapy procedures for helping clients identify these mistaken beliefs, challenge them, and develop new, more effective beliefs. We will look at a variety of these techniques as we discuss methods for managing each specific denial pattern.

Putting the Denial Identification Process Together: We have just broken the denial identification process into its component parts. Now let's consciously link those parts back together and show how the fluid and dynamic process works. The behavioral goal, the self-talk, and the mistaken beliefs are related to the clients nonverbal behavior and the therapist's gut reaction.

The client firmly holds this mistaken belief: *If I don't think or talk about a problem it won't be a problem anymore.* The client will now select the behavioral goal of either not talking about anything related to the problem (the avoidance pattern) *or convincing self and others the problem doesn't exist* (the absolute denial pattern).

If the client chooses avoidance they will engage in compulsive self-talk about other things they decide are more important than the real problem, and their behavioral goal will be to subtly steer people away from seeing the problem by getting them to think and talk about other things. As a result their behavior shifts from genuine communication into controlling and continuously refocusing the communication. When they do this there are verbal and nonverbal shifts. The shift in behavior is picked up intuitively by the therapist in the form of a gut reaction that "something is wrong" or "something has changed." Then the therapist begins to consciously notice the nonverbal indicators and begins to describe consciously in their own mind the dynamic that is unfolding in the session.

The therapist will then be ready to move to the next step of denial management, which is exposing the denial pattern to the client. It is important to remember that each denial pattern has its unique behavioral goals, cognitive themes and self talk patterns, and mistaken beliefs. As a result, they produce different verbal and nonverbal behaviors that tend to activate different "gut reactions" in the therapist.

Application to the Twelve Denial Patterns

There are twelve basic denial patterns. To study them in a manageable way we will break them down into two groups: the Big Five and the Small Seven. You will need to know all of these denial patterns and their variations to work effectively with clients. Although the following information is precise and technical, it is helpful to think of it as both *learning a procedure* and *training your clinical intuition.*

When we learn the procedure of denial management we intellectually understand a process and learn the behavioral skills necessary to use that process with clients. By learning the procedures we are training the creative, intuitive, and unconscious parts of our minds to automatically recognize and respond appropriately when denial occurs. The more we consciously practice recognizing and appropriately responding to denial, the more the process will be automated, habituated, and integrated into our clinical intuition. Once this has occurred you will be able to both hear and sense what denial pattern is being used.

We will take you through the process of dealing directly with each of the twelve denial patterns later. For now, remember the five steps in identifying when a client starts using denial: (1) Listen to your gut; (2) look for nonverbal indicators; (3) identify the behavior goals; (4) Identify the cognitive theme; and (5) identify the mistaken beliefs. Once this is done you are ready to expose the denial pattern to the client.

MRC Interactional Process (steps 4–7): Once you have identified the denial patterns being used you can now expose, educate, challenge, and teach self-management

(4) **Exposing Denial:** Expose the denial pattern so clients can see what they are doing.

(5) **Educating about Denial:** Educate about the denial pattern so clients can understand why the denial pattern won't work.

(6) **Challenging Denial:** Challenge the denial pattern by giving a therapeutic injunction against continued use of denial and therapeutic permission to look honestly at the core problem, and by pointing out the logical, negative consequences of continuing to use denial.

(7) **Teaching Denial Self-Management:** Teach denial self-management methods so the client can recognize and stop their own denial when it starts to interfere with their recovery.

Let's take a close look at how to effectively expose denial to a client so they can recognize and accept the behaviors they are using and see that continued denial won't work.

Step 4: Exposing the Denial Pattern

You expose the denial pattern by naming it and presenting its cognitive theme and related self-talk to the client. This is done in the paraphrasing step of active listening.

For example, if a client refuses to answer questions directly and keeps changing the subject, you can use this as a paraphrase: *"What I'm hearing you say is that you would rather talk about anything except the real problem that caused you to seek treatment. Is that correct?"*

This method names the denial pattern and exposes the cognitive theme and related self-talk. It also exposes the hidden agenda of the denial pattern that carries with it *the invitation to become part of the problem.* In the case of avoidance, the invitation is to become part of the problem by talking about something. Once the denial pattern, its theme, and the invitation are openly discussed, the conscious hidden agenda becomes public and the manipulation loses its power. This method of exposing the denial pattern can be called "name the game" or "name the strategy." Once the unconscious game is out in the open, its power is diffused. Once the denial pattern is exposed, clients usually stop using that specific denial pattern. Unfortunately, most clients don't return to genuine communication and problem solving. They usually shift to a different denial pattern.

A natural tendency is to go with the flow and begin the active listening process with the new denial pattern. If you do this, clients will almost certainly start using the previous denial pattern at some time in the future.

Most clients exhibiting hard-core denial have a preferred defensive structure of three to six denial patterns. They move easily from one denial pattern to another. Before you can expose and defuse one pattern, they shift to another pattern and invite you to come along for the ride. Just as you are getting a handle on the new pattern, they shift again. In this way, clients using hard-core denial keep the therapist off balance, and the client avoids having to consciously recognize and deal with any one denial pattern.

When clients try to shift to a different denial pattern, it is important to learn how to stop the process by staying focused on the first denial pattern used. This is done by taking charge of the session and by shifting from an *Interviewing Mode* based on active listening to a *Mini-Education Mode* based on educating the client about the denial pattern.

Step 5: Educating about the Denial Pattern

The goal of educating clients about the denial pattern is to keep the client focused on the denial pattern that was exposed. You want to have the client clearly see what that denial pattern is so they can become consciously aware of its theme or message and the fundamental mistaken belief on which it is based.

One way to do this is to stop the session and say something like this: "Excuse me, I'm a little bit confused. I just said that *repeat the exposing statement from step 2* and I asked you if that was correct. It seems like you just shifted gears and went on to something else. I want to spend a few minutes talking about *Name the denial pattern again and present a mini-education session.*" In this way you can bring the client back into a position of dealing with the denial pattern that was exposed without engaging in a direct confrontation that could lead to a power struggle.

A mini-education session is a one-minute educational overview of the denial pattern. Here is the suggested mini-education session for avoidance:

Mini-Education Session #1: Avoidance: "*Listening to you reminds me of a client I once treated named Jake. They called him Jake the Snake because he was so slippery. He was the best I've ever seen at using a form of denial called avoidance. No matter what question I asked Jake, he could avoid answering it by shifting the focus to something else. That's what avoidance is all about—getting people to talk about anything except the real problem. Jake was real good at it. He believed that if he could avoid talking about his drinking and drug problem, it would just go away. Unfortunately, Jake's dead. He relapsed and got killed in a drunk-driving accident.*"

Notice that the above mini-education session used the example of another client to name the denial pattern, expose its theme, explain the mistaken belief on which it is based, and then show the logical consequences of staying in denial.

When using mini-education sessions about a denial pattern it is helpful to have brief but memorable stories or analogies that expose the dynamics and hidden flaws of the denial pattern. In the next section I will examine each denial pattern and give specific examples of how to educate and share some stories and analogies that have proven to be helpful. For now I'll just give one additional example.

Suppose a client is using absolute denial. This client was arrested for a second DUI and reports that his wife is upset with his arrest and that he is concerned that if his boss finds out he may be fired. Then he asserts that he doesn't have a drinking problem and alcohol has "nothing to do with the reason he was arrested."

I would expose the denial pattern by saying something like this: *"It sounds to me that you are absolutely denying that you have any problems with drinking. You seem to be saying that just because you were arrested for a DUI doesn't mean you have a drinking problem. Is that correct?"*

I might then say something like this: *"You know that reminds me of a man who was standing on a railroad track looking at an express train coming straight at him from way down the track. The man solved the problem by turning around and looking down the track in the other direction. He breathed a sigh of relief and said to himself, 'Thank God, now I don't have to worry. There's no train coming!'"*

Notice how the mini-education session stops the client from shifting the focus, puts the therapist back firmly in charge of the session, and puts out important information in the form of a story about someone or something else. These stories, analogies, and metaphors can imprint the information on the client's mind. And because it is just a story, the client has a hard time developing a counterattack.

The best defense they can usually come up with is to ask, *"What has that got to do with me?"* To which you can say, *"Probably nothing. I don't know why that story came to my mind. What were we talking about? Oh yes, we were talking about how I thought you were trying to avoid looking at the problems that brought you here."*

Step 6: Challenging the Denial Pattern

Once the denial pattern is *exposed* and the patient is *educated* with a mini-education session, the next step is to *challenge* the denial pattern. When challenging a denial pattern or any other irrational thought, it is important to do three things: (1) Point out the problem with using the denial pattern by showing the logical consequences of staying in denial; (2) give a *therapeutic injunction* against using the denial pattern; and (3) Give *therapeutic permission* to stop using denial and to deal directly with the core problem.

Pointing Out the Problem with Using that Denial Pattern: The first step in dealing with a denial pattern is to point out the problem with using that denial pattern to solve the problem: In dealing with avoidance, for example, you can say something like this: *"The problem with using avoidance is that it doesn't work. Jake found that out the hard way. He died a horrible death in a drunk-driving accident. I'm sure his last words were, 'If I don't think about how bad this accident is, it will go away!' Unfortunately, most problems don't just go away. If we don't deal with them they just keep getting worse.*

"There was once a carpenter who had an accident with a power saw. He cut the artery in his wrist. What would happen to him if he managed to convince himself that the cut artery would go away if he didn't think or talk about the fact he was bleeding to death?

"Do you see the problem with avoiding taking an honest look at serious problems. Can you see where this situation is going if you refuse to look honestly at the truth about what is happening?"

Using Therapeutic Injunctions to Challenge Denial: The second step in challenging the denial pattern is to give a therapeutic injunction against using that denial pattern by saying something like this: "You don't have to deny that the train's coming. You don't have to pretend that getting a DUI has nothing to do with your drinking. Denying the problem won't work. You deserve better than that!"

Using Therapeutic Permission to Challenge Denial: The third step is to give the client therapeutic permission to deal directly with the core problem. You can do this by saying something like, *"It's OK to look honestly at the issue of your DUI and your drinking. You can face the problem honestly, figure out the truth, and decide on the best way to handle the situa-*

tion. If you try to turn your back on the problem and pretend it's not there, you will end up getting blindsided later on."

So remember this three-step dynamic process: (1) Point out the problem with using the denial pattern (*"The problem with using* name the denial pattern *is that it doesn't work. If you keep trying to solve the problem this way it will end by* describe a probably negative outcome"); (2) Give a therapeutic injunction against using the denial pattern (*"You don't have to use* name the denial pattern *because it won't work for you!"*; and (3) give therapeutic permission to deal with the problem openly and honestly (*"You can face the truth about what's really going on and figure out the best way to handle it."*).

Timing is a critical factor in using statements of therapeutic permission and injunction. The client must be in a receptive state of consciousness. This state is created by the story, analogy, or metaphor used in the mini-education session. If you tell the story effectively, the client will stop and listen. They will momentarily shut down their active denial process as they get into the story, and a brief window of opportunity will open. This is when you drop in the statements of therapeutic injunction and permission. What these statements do is plant a suggestion in the client's mind that starts to undermine the power of the denial strategy.

One therapist I trained called these **Time Bombs of Recovery** or **Therapeutic Time Bombs.** They often don't have an immediate effect in the short run, but the clients just can't seem to get them out of their mind. Every time they try to use the denial pattern the analogy, story, or image pops into their mind. As more and more of these recovery time bombs get planted, the denial dynamics begin to break down.

When you start to sense the breakdown of the denial pattern and a willingness to think about the problem in a different way, it is time to move into a mini-education session about denial pattern management. This takes the education process from the level of information to the level of action or behavioral skill.

Step 7: Teaching Denial Pattern Management

The final step is to teach the client how to recognize and stop the denial pattern and to focus the client on learning the skills needed to identify and solve their problems. The alternative to denial is recognition, acceptance, and problem solving.

One standard way of teaching clients to manage denial patterns is the use of a **self-monitoring technique.** Explain to the client that is important for them to recognize when they start using the denial pattern so they can consciously choose whether to avoid or deal with the problem. Ask them to agree to an experiment. Tell them you want to repeat the sequence of questions that just activated the denial pattern. Instead of focusing just on the answer to the questions, you want them to focus on the private thoughts and feelings that go through their head as they answer the questions. Then review with the client the cognitive theme of the denial pattern and ask clients to monitor themselves for the signs they are slipping into their old habit of using denial patterns.

It is helpful to set up a signal that clients can use to stop the session and talk about the here-and-now communication or the thoughts or feelings they are having. I like to use the "time-out signal" that the referees use in football games. Ask the client to use the time-out signal anytime they sense themselves starting to use the denial pattern.

It is also important for the therapist to get the client's permission to use the time-out signal if they think the client is slipping back into avoidance. The goal of self-management is to be able to change the focus of the session from answering questions about the target problem to examining the here-and-now communication process that is preventing the client from looking at the problem.

In Part 3 of this book, Advanced Clinical Skills, each of the intervention steps of the Denial Management Interactional Process is specifically applied to each of the twelve denial patterns. Before going to that level, let's explore the clinical exercises that make up the specific content of a denial management treatment plan.

2–4: Denial Management Counseling—Clinical Exercises

Denial Management Counseling (DMC) has been organized

into nine clinical exercises that can be used in individual therapy, problem-solving group therapy, or psychoeducation programs. Each exercise explains some basic information about denial or denial management and then asks a series of questions to help clients apply that information to their current situation. These nine clinical exercises form the basis of *The Denial Management Counseling (DMC) Workbook.* This workbook is an excellent tool for giving clients homework assignments that accelerate the therapy process. You don't need to use the workbook to do denial management counseling. Once you understand the underlying principles you can integrate the steps of each exercise into your clinical style and adapt the exercises creatively as needed in your clinical practice.

This section briefly describes each of the Denial Management Clinical Exercises in words that I would use if describing them to a client going through the process. This will help you see how I would phrase and explain points of information and how I would ask questions. For these exercises to work for you, you will need to personalize them so they reflect your clinical style.

In the following exercise I have used the concept of Mini-Education sessions to explain the basic information that clients need to understand. These mini-education sessions are followed by a series of questions to help the client apply the information to themselves. Each question needs to be processed using active listening.

Exercise #1: Understanding Denial as a Part of the Human Condition:

Mini-Education Session: This is an educational exercise that explains that denial is a normal and natural part of the human condition related to our need to search for the truth about what is happening to us despite our tendency to make mistakes and lie to ourselves. We are all fragile and can be easily hurt when we make mistakes. This creates the tendency for us to lie to ourselves when we do make mistakes in order to avoid the pain. We are all capable of convincing ourselves that the lies are, in fact, true. Once we start believing our own lies, we tend to become deceptive and can start lying to others whether we mean to or not. As a result, we all need to develop personal and social systems for finding the truth while protecting ourselves from self-deception and the lies of others. Denial management is a personal system for finding the truth while protecting ourselves from self-deception.

This information is integrated by using active listening to process the following questions: (1) Do you want to know the truth about what is happening in your life? Tell me about that. (2) Have you spent time trying to answer questions like, "Who am I? Why am I here? How do I fit in? What is my place in the world? What does the world require of me in order to survive and thrive?" (3) Have things happened in your life that have caused you to ask, "What is wrong with me?" and (4) Are you interested in figuring out what you must do in order to identify and solve your problems, stop your pain and suffering, and live a life that is meaningful?

Denial Check: Each exercise ends with several questions, called a denial check, to see if the client's denial was activated while answering the questions. I'll list the questions here. In describing the other exercises I will simply note that you need to complete a denial check at this point. The questions in the denial check are as follows: (1) Did your stress go up as you talked with me about these questions? (Denial is normally activated by sensitive questions that activate a "hot response" in the client.) (2) Did an inner conflict or argument start in your head as you talked with me about these questions? (3) Did you feel an urge to avoid answering the questions or to tell lies or half truths? Tell me about that.

Exercise 1–2: The Tendency to Make Mistakes

1. Do you believe the world can be a confusing place and that the truth can be difficult to find? Tell me about that.

2. Do you believe we learn about the world from other people (such as our parents, relatives, or friends) who might be wrong? Tell me about that.

3. Do you believe we are programmed to learn by trial and error, so we must periodically make mistakes in order to learn? Tell me about that.

4. Do you sometimes think that if something makes you feel good in the moment it must be true, and if something makes you feel bad in the moment, it must not be true? Tell me about that.

5. Do you ever get set in your ways, refuse to admit you are wrong, and keep doing things that don't work very well for you? Tell me about that.

6. End this part of the interview with a denial check.

Exercise 1–3: The Tendency to Lie to Ourselves

1. Have there been times in your life when you tended to see things in a way that caused you the least amount of pain and gave you the easiest solution or way out? Tell me about that.

2. Have there been times in your life when you have told yourself a lie and then started to believe that your own lies were true? Tell me about that.

3. How do you currently test your beliefs to determine if they are actually true or if you are lying to yourself? Tell me about that.

4. End this part of the interview with a denial check.

Exercise 1–4: The Tendency to Lie to Others:

Mini-Education Session: Sometimes we lie to others because we feel that something bad will happen to us if we don't or because we believe that lying is the best way to get something we want.

1. Have you ever consciously or deliberately lied to other people? Tell me about that.

2. Have you ever lied to others because you felt threatened or believed that something bad would happen to you if you told the truth? Tell me about that.

3. Have you ever lied in order to get something you wanted? Tell me about that.

4. Do you believe that lying can help you get what you want out of your treatment? Tell me about that.

5. End this part of the interview with a denial check.

Exercise 1–5: Denial as a Normal Defense Against Pain, Guilt, and Shame

Mini-Education Session: Denial is a normal and natural psychological defense. Just as the human body has an immune system to protect it from dangerous physical organisms, the human mind has a *mental immune system* to protect it from overwhelming pain and problems. That mental immune system is called a psychological defense system. The goal of this **psychological defense system** is to protect the integrity of our mind and personality.

Denial is activated whenever we are asked to think or talk about a painful or overwhelming problem. There is nothing sick, pathological, or wrong about this. Denial is a normal and natural human response to severe pain and problems. Everyone uses denial every day, especially when we are under a lot of stress. Denial gets turned on by triggers that cause intense stress and starts mobilizing automatic defensive thoughts and the urge to use resistant behaviors. These defensive reactions are normal and natural. Anyone who has a serious problem or illness will tend to deny it. People with good sobriety and mental health skills will learn how to recognize and stop the denial early, before the denial causes serious problems.

1. *Imagine yourself in this situation.* You are at work and suddenly begin to feel a pain in your chest. At first the pain isn't very bad, but it slowly starts to get worse. The pain keeps getting worse and worse.

1–A. How bad would the pain have to get for you to consider your chest pain to be a serious problem?

1–B. How bad would the pain have to get for you to ask someone to call an ambulance because you are having a heart attack?

1–C. Do you think you might deny the pain and try to tough it out until you couldn't work or collapsed on the job?

2. *Imagine yourself in this situation:* You believe you are a social drinker or a recreational drug user. You honestly don't believe you have any problems with your alcohol or drug use. Things start going wrong in your life, but you are convinced they have nothing to do with drinking or drugging. Things keep

getting worse and people you know start telling you your problems are caused by your drinking and drugging. You don't believe them. You do your best to solve your problems but keep on drinking socially and using drugs recreationally.

2–A. How bad would things have to get for you to consider you might have a drinking or drug problem?

2–B. How bad would things have to get for you to ask for help with your alcohol or drug problem?

2–C. Do you think you might deny the pain and problems caused by your alcohol and drug use and try to tough it out until you lost your friends, hurt your family, lost your job, or got sent to jail?

3. End this part of the interview with a denial check.

Exercise #2: Understanding the Principles of Denial Management

Mini-Education Session: This exercise explains the basic information you will need to understand and recognize denial. I want you to be able to make a choice between continuing to lie to yourself or facing and dealing with the truth about what is happening in your life.

Denial is the natural tendency to avoid the pain that is caused by thinking and talking about serious problems. This pain is avoided by using a set of automatic and unconscious thoughts, feelings, and actions that keep us from thinking and talking about our problems. Denial is a normal psychological defense that has both benefits and disadvantages. The major benefit of using denial is that it allows us to avoid feeling the pain caused by serious or overwhelming problems. The major disadvantage is that it prevents us from seeing what is really going on and effectively managing our problems.

The primary feelings that drive denial are pain, anger, fear, guilt, and shame. Denial can be recognized. You can face the truth about what is happening in your life, and by doing this you can turn your life around.

Exercise 2–1: The Benefits and Disadvantages of Using Denial

1. What are three benefits you could get from denying the problems that brought you into treatment?

2. What are three disadvantages or problems you could get from denying the problems that brought you into treatment?

3. Did you ever suddenly get in trouble and not understand why, only to discover later that your problem was obvious to everyone except you? Tell me about that.

4. End this part of the interview with a denial check.

Exercise 2–2: Acceptance and Problem-Solving as Antidotes for Denial

Mini-Education Session: There are two antidotes for denial: acceptance and problem-solving.

Acceptance is a peaceful acknowledgment of the truth. If we can calmly face the problem, acknowledge the truth about what is going on, and accept that it is happening to us, we can then develop a way for handling the situation.

Problem-Solving is a system for finding solutions to our problems.

Effective problem-solving systems involve identification and clarification of our problems, identifying and projecting the logical consequences of alternatives, deciding which alternative to use, taking action, and evaluating the outcome.

By recognizing and accepting the problem and developing an effective problem-solving plan, our need to use denial will go down because our ability to manage our problems will go up.

1. Can you think of a time when you were able to solve a serious problem because you were forced to look at what was really going on and to deal with it? Describe that experience.

2. When you decide that something is going wrong in your life and you need to deal with it before it gets worse, what are the steps you normally go through to figure out what is wrong and to fix it?

3. Are you satisfied with your current ability to see what is really going wrong in your life and to use effective methods to solve the problems?

4. End this part of the interview with a denial check.

Exercise 2–3: Denial Can Be Recognized and Managed

Mini-Education Session: We can learn to recognize and manage our denial by noticing what happens inside us when our denial gets turned on. When denial is turned on our stress levels go up, we get irritable and can easily get angry, we start to feel fearful, threatened, or unsure of ourselves for no good reason, and we start having an inner conflict or argument in our heads, (i.e., one part of us wants to avoid looking at the problem; another part of us wants to take a good, honest look at what is really going on and set up a plan to solve the problem).

The first step in learning how to manage our denial is to learn how to sit still and notice what is going on inside us. We need to learn how to notice what we are thinking, especially our inner conflicts and conversations, our feelings, and our urges to do things. By noticing what is going on inside us, we can make conscious decisions about what we want to do before we blindly act out. Remember our goal: *To think it through before we act it out.*

1. Do you believe that you sometimes use denial when it would be better for you to recognize what is really happening and set up a plan to deal with it? Tell me about that.

2. When you think you might be using denial, what can you do to check yourself out and see if you are using denial or honestly looking at the problem?

3. Once you see what the real problem is, what steps do you normally use to solve the problem?

4. End this part of the interview with a denial check.

Exercise 2–4: Defining Denial in a Way that Can Help Manage It

Mini-Education Session: Denial is a set of automatic and unconscious thoughts, feelings, and actions that protect us from the pain of thinking about and talking about our problems. When we say that denial is *automatic,* we mean that we do it spontaneously when something happens to us. Anything that forces us to think or talk about our problems can activate or trigger denial. When we say that denial is *unconscious,* we mean that we do it without thinking. When we start to think or talk about our problems, intense feelings get turned on and these feelings activate our denial. When our denial is turned on, we start to have distracting thoughts, feelings, and behaviors that shift our focus from the problem to one of the distractions. This means we have to constantly monitor ourselves or we can easily lapse into denial without evening knowing it.

So, to manage our denial we must continuously pay attention to three things: (1) What do we start *to think* about that keeps us from facing our problems? (2) What do we start *to feel* that keeps us from facing our problems? (3) What do we start *to do* that that keeps us from facing our problems? We must be able to answer these three question in order to recognize and solve our problems instead of making them worse by denying them. This means that we need to learn how to stay calm and detached while thinking and talking about our problems. This may be harder than it appears because denial is an automatic and unconscious reaction that raises our stress, scrambles our thinking, and causes us to overreact emotionally.

There is a simple experiment that can tell you if you are using denial. First, think about and write down the answers to the following three questions (Questions 1–3). Then we'll discuss your answers.

1. What are the three most serious problems going on in your life right now?

2. How would you rate the seriousness of each problem using a ten-point scale? (10=very serious, 1=not at all serious). Why do you rate each one that way?

3. Do you believe you are responsible for solving these problem?

As you think about, write down, and discuss the answers to these questions notice what happened inside of you and answer the following questions (Questions 4, 5, and 6).

4. Did your stress level change as you answered the questions?

5. Did you experience any inner conflicts? (Did one part of

you start saying one thing while another part of you says something else?)

6. Did you feel an urge to avoid answering the questions, tell lies or half truths, or avoid responsibility by blaming someone else?

Exercise 2–5: The Feelings that Drive Denial

Mini-Education Session: The primary feelings that drive denial are pain, anger, fear, guilt, and shame. We feel *pain* because we are facing difficult and seemingly overwhelming problems that are destroying our lives. We feel *anger* because the problems seem unfair and there is nothing we can do about them. We feel *fear* because we are out of control and don't know how to handle the problems. We feel *guilt* because, on some level, we believe we are having these painful problems because we have done something wrong or immoral. We feel *shame* because we believe, on some level, that we are defective as human beings because we have these problems.

We can temporarily turn off these feelings by using denial, but these feelings almost always come back later. When they come back, we use denial once again to make the feelings go away for a little while. When they come back again later we use more denial. We keep doing this over and over again until using denial becomes an automatic and unconscious habit for handling painful feelings. Because thinking and talking about serious problems almost always causes painful feelings, we actually get in the habit of using denial to manage our problems and never learn other ways to solve our problems. This means that, in many ways, *denial is the last refuge of the incompetent*. We use denial when we don't know any other way to manage our pain or solve our problems. Most of the time we are not even consciously aware we are using denial.

1. When you think or talk about the problems that caused you to come into treatment, do you ever feel *pain or hurt*? If you do, how intense is the feeling (1=not intense; 10=very intense)? Why did you rate it that way?

2. When you think or talk about the problems that caused you to come into treatment, do you ever feel *mad or angry*? If

you do, how intense is the feeling (1=not intense; 10=very intense)? Why did you rate it that way?

3. When you think or talk about the problems that caused you to come into treatment, do you ever feel *afraid or anxious*? If you do, how intense is the feeling (1=not intense; 10=very intense)? Why did you rate it that way?

4. When you think or talk about the problems that caused you to come into treatment, do you ever feel *guilt or shame*? If you do, how intense is the feeling (1=not intense; 10=very intense)? Why did you rate it that way?

5. Did you ever try to get rid of these feelings by using denial in an attempt to convince yourself you didn't have these problems? If you do, how intense is the feeling (1=not intense; 10=very intense)? Why did you rate it that way?

Exercise #3: Recognizing Your Denial Patterns

This exercise describes twelve common denial patterns that people tend to use to deny they have serious problems with alcohol or other drugs. You will be asked to review a denial pattern checklist that explains these denial patterns and to select and personalize the three denial patterns that you tend to use most often.

Exercise 3–1: Reviewing the Denial Pattern Checklist

Mini-Education Session: In this exercise we will read a list that describes the twelve common denial patterns. The goal is for you to understand the denial patterns and recognize the ones you tend to use. Before we start reading the list, let's take a moment to calm down, get centered, and relax. Take a deep breath. Hold it for a moment. Then slowly exhale and let yourself become deeply relaxed.

Now let's read the list of denial patterns out loud. As we read, listen carefully to what the description of each denial pattern is trying to tell you. I'll ask you the following questions after we read each warning sign.

1. As you read this warning sign did your stress go up? Did an inner conflict or argument start in your head? Did you space

out, get confused, or feel an urge to stop reading?

2. Have you ever seen other people using this denial pattern? If you have, describe how you saw them use this denial pattern.

3. Have you ever used this denial pattern? If you have, describe a situation in which you used this warning sign.

Let's start reading.

Denial Pattern #1. Avoidance: I say to myself: *"I'll talk about anything but my real problems!"* Somewhere deep inside me I am afraid I might have a problem with alcohol or drugs that is hurting me and those I care about. But when I don't think or talk about it, I feel OK. So I think about other things and try to keep people from prying into my life where they don't belong. My drinking and drugging is private and no one has a right to know anything about it. If someone asks about it, I change the subject and start talking about other things that have nothing to do with my drinking and drugging. If nothing else works, I'll start an uproar by creating a bad crisis and making sure they get sucked into it. If all else fails I'll play dumb and pretend I don't know what they're talking about.

Denial Pattern #2. Absolute Denial: I say to myself: *"No, not me! I don't have a problem!"* When others try to corner me, I tell "the big lie." I say I don't have a problem with alcohol or drugs. No, not me! Absolutely not! I don't drink too much! I don't use drugs!; I'm not addicted! I never get sick or have problems because of drinking or drugging. I am so good at convincing other people there is nothing wrong that sometimes I actually start believing it myself. When they believe my story a part of me feels really good because I beat them. Another small part of me feels disappointed. There is a small part that wants others to know what is really happening. There is a small, scared part inside me that wants help.

Denial Pattern #3. Minimizing: I say to myself: *"My problems aren't that bad!"* Sometimes my alcohol and drug problems get so bad I can't convince myself or others that I don't have a problem. When this happens I minimize. I make the problems seem smaller than they really are. Yes, I had a small problem with my drinking and drugging, but it only happened once. It will never happen again. Besides, the problem just wasn't as bad as people think it is.

Denial Pattern #4. Rationalizing: I say to myself: *"If I can find good enough reasons for my problems, I won't have to deal with them!"* I try to explain away my alcohol and drug problems by making up good explanations for why I drink and what's "really" causing my problems. Sometimes I'll pretend to know a lot about alcoholism and addiction so other people will think I know too much to have a problem. The truth is that I rarely if ever apply what I know to myself or to my own problems.

Denial Pattern #5. Blaming: I say to myself: *"If I can prove that my problems are not my fault, I won't have to deal with them!"* When the problems get so bad I can't deny them, I find a scapegoat. I tell everyone that it's not my fault I have these problems with alcohol and drugs. It's somebody else's fault. I only abuse alcohol and drugs because of my partner. If you were with a person like this, you'd abuse alcohol and drugs too! If you had a job or a boss like mine, you'd drink and drug as much as I do. As long as I can blame someone else, I can keep drinking and drugging until that person changes. I don't have to be responsible for stopping.

Denial Pattern #6. Comparing: I say to myself: *"Showing that others are worse than me proves that I don't have serious problems!"* I start to focus on other people instead of myself. I find others who have more serious alcohol and drug problems than I do and compare myself to them. I tell myself I can't be addicted because I'm not as bad as they are. I know what an addict is! An addict is someone who drinks and drugs a lot more than I do! An addict is someone who has a lot more alcohol and drug-related problems than I do. An addict is someone who is not like me! I tell myself I can't be addicted because there are other people who have worse problems with alcohol and drugs than I do.

Denial Pattern #7. Compliance: I say to myself: *"I'll pretend to do what you want, if you'll leave me alone!"* I start going through the motions of getting help. I do what I'm told, no more and no less. I become compliant and promise to do things just to get people off my back. I find excuses for not following through. When I get caught, I tell people I did the best I could. I blame them for not giving me enough help. I tell people how sorry I am. I ask for another chance, make another half-hearted commitment, and the cycle of compliance starts all over again.

Denial Pattern #8. Manipulating: I say to myself: *"I'll only admit that I have problems if you agree to solve them for me!"* When my alcohol and drug problems box me into a corner, I start to manipulate. I try to use the people who want to help me. I try to get them to handle all of my problems and then get them to leave me alone so I can keep drinking and drugging. I'll let them help me, but only if they do it for me. I want a quick, effortless fix. If I they can't fix me, I blame them for my failure and use them as an excuse to keep drinking and drugging. I won't let anyone make me do anything I don't want to do. If they try, I'll get angry at them, blame them, and make them feel guilty.

Denial Pattern #9. Flight into Health: I say to myself: *"Feeling better means that I'm cured!"* I manage to stay clean and sober for awhile and things start to get a little bit better. Instead of getting motivated to do more, I convince myself that I'm cured and don't need to do anything. I tell myself I may have had a drinking and drug problem, but I got into recovery and put it behind me.

Denial Pattern #10. Recovery by Fear: I say to myself: *"Being scared of my problems will make them go away!"* I began to realize that alcohol and other drugs can destroy my life, hurt those I love, and eventually kill me. The threat is so real that I convince myself I can't ever use alcohol or drugs again. I start to believe this fear of destroying my life and killing myself will scare me into permanent sobriety. Because I now know how awful my life will be if I continue to drink and drug, I just won't drink or drug anymore. If I just stop everything will be fine. Because everything will be fine, I won't need treatment or a recovery program. I'll just quit.

Denial Pattern #11. Strategic Hopelessness: I say to myself: *"Since nothing works, I don't have to try."* I start to feel I'm hopeless. It seems like I've done it all and nothing works. I don't believe I can change and a big part of me just doesn't want to try anymore. It's easier just to give up. When people try to help me, I brush them off by telling them I'm hopeless and will never recover. When people do try to help me, I give them a hard time and make it impossible for them to help me. I don't understand why people want to help me. It would be easier if they just let me keep drinking and drugging.

Denial Pattern #12. The Democratic Disease State: I say to myself: *"I have the right to destroy myself and no one has the right to stop me!"* I convince myself I have a right to continue to use alcohol and drugs even if it kills me. Yes, I'm addicted. Yes, I'm destroying my life. Yes, I'm hurting those I love. Yes, I'm a burden to society. But so what? I have the right to drink and drug myself to death. No one has the right to make me stop. My addiction is killing me anyway, so I might as well convince myself I'm dying because I want to.

Exercise 3–2: Learning How to Personalize Denial Patterns

In order to learn how to recognize and manage our own denial, we need to learn how to personalize the denial patterns we selected. We personalize denial patterns by writing a new title and description for each one in our own words. For example, I could rewrite the title for avoidance as "Beating around the bush" or "Skating off the walls."

The next step is to write a description of the denial pattern that begins with the words: "I know I'm using denial when I…". Notice the word "I" at the end of this phrase. The denial pattern is written in the first person. This means you need to be the person who is the subject of the sentence.

Here are some examples of personalized denial patterns. I have also placed this list in *Appendix 3: Samples of Personalized Denial Patterns* so you can easily review it with your clients.

1. (Avoidance) **Skating off the Walls:** I know I'm using denial when I refuse to directly answer a question and keep trying to change the subject.

2. (Absolute Denial) **Saying It Isn't So:** I know I'm using denial when I tell people I don't have a problem even though I know deep inside I do.

3. (Minimizing) **Saying It Isn't that Bad:** I know I'm using denial when I admit I have a problem but try to tell people it isn't as bad as they think it is.

4. (Rationalizing) **Giving Good Reasons:** I know I'm using denial when I try to convince people there are good reasons for me to have the problem and because there are good reasons I shouldn't be responsible for having to deal with it.

5. (Blaming) **Saying It's Not My Fault:** I know I'm using denial when I try to blame someone else for my problem and deny that I am responsible for dealing with it.

6. (Comparison) **Criticizing Others:** I know I'm using denial when I point out how bad other people's problems are and use that as a reason why my problems aren't so bad.

7. (Compliance) **Being a Good Little Boy:** I know I'm using denial when I start telling people what they want to hear to get them off my back.

8. (Manipulating) **Getting Over on Others:** I know I'm using denial when I try to get other people to handle the problems for me.

9. (Flight into Health) **Suddenly Cured:** I know I'm using denial when I believe my problems have suddenly gone away without my doing anything to solve them.

10. (Recovery by Fear) **Scared Straight:** I know I'm using denial when I tell myself I could never use alcohol or drugs again because I'm so afraid of what will happen if I start drinking and drugging.

11. (Strategic Hopelessness) **Why Bother?:** I know I'm using denial when I tell myself I can never solve my problems and that other people should just leave me alone.

12. (Democratic Disease State) **I Have My Rights:** I know I'm using denial when I tell other people I have a right to use alcohol and drugs regardless of what happens and that they have no right to try and stop me.

Exercise 3–3: Selecting the Denial Patterns that You Tend to Use

Select three denial patterns you have used in the past. Write down the title of the three denial patterns, putting the denial patterns you tend to use most frequently first on the list.

Exercise 3–4: Personalizing the Denial Patterns

Personalize each of those denial patterns by answering the following questions about each one.

1. What is the denial pattern you selected?

2. Why did you select this denial pattern?

3. Go back to the *Denial Pattern Checklist* and read the description of the denial pattern again. Underline what you consider the most important word or phrase. What word or phrase did you underline?

4. What does this word or phrase mean to you?

5. Write *a personal title* for this denial pattern that will be easy for you to remember. The title should be no longer than two or three words.

6. Write *a personal description* for this denial pattern. Make sure the description is a single sentence that begins with the words, "*I know I'm going into denial when I start to…*". Don't use any of the words from your personal title in this personal description.

Repeat this sequence of questions for all three denial patterns the client selected. Be sure to have the client write down the denial patterns neatly on a sheet of paper.

Exercise #4: Managing Denial

In this exercise you will learn how to identify the thoughts, feelings, urges, actions, and social reactions associated with the three denial patterns you selected and personalized. Then we will learn how to turn off each denial pattern by changing what we are thinking, how we are managing our feelings and urges, what we are doing, and how we are relating to other people.

Mini-Education Session: The first thing we need to do is to understand how thoughts, feelings, urges, actions, and social reactions relate to one another. Here are some basic principles that can help us understand how this works.

1. *Thoughts Cause Feelings.* Whenever we think about something we automatically react by having a feeling or an emotion.

2. *Thoughts and Feelings Work Together to Cause Urges.* Our way of thinking causes us to feel certain things. These feelings, in turn, reinforce the way we are thinking. These thoughts and feelings work together to create an urge to do something. An urge is a desire that may be rational or irrational. The irrational urge to use alcohol or other drugs, even though we know it will hurt us, is also called *craving.* It is irrational because we want to use alcohol or other drugs even though we know it will not be good for us.

3. *Urges Plus Decisions Cause Actions.* When we feel an urge we can pause and decide to do something about it or do nothing. This pause between the urge and action is called a decision point. Decision points are critically important because what we do or don't do at a decision point will determine what happens next.

A decision is a choice. A choice is a specific way of thinking that causes us to commit to one way of doing things while refusing to do anything else. The decision point is the space between the urge and the action, and it is always filled with a decision. The decision may be an automatic and unconscious choice we have learned to make without having to think about it, or the decision can be based on a conscious choice that results from carefully reflecting on the situation and the options available for dealing with it.

4. *Actions Cause Reactions from Other People.* Our actions affect other people and cause them to react to us. It is helpful to think about our behavior like invitations that we give to other people to treat us in certain ways. Some behaviors invite people to be nice and treat us with respect. Other behaviors invite people to argue and fight with us or to put us down. In every social situation we share part of the responsibility for what happens. This is because we are constantly inviting people to respond to us by the actions we take and by how we react to what other people do.

To recognize and stop our denial we need to learn how to

(1) tell the difference between thoughts and feelings; (2) tell the difference between feelings and urges; (3) tell the difference between urges and actions; and (4) tell the difference between our actions and the social reaction they cause.

Learning how to manage our denial patterns teaches us *how to control our impulses*. We don't have to do whatever we feel an urge to do. We can learn to stop our automatic reactions and start to make conscious choices. We can do this by learning how to *pause, relax, reflect, and decide*. We can learn to control our impulses even when we feel a strong urge to do something immediately. It's not easy, but we can learn how.

Let's look at these four steps of the impulse control process: (1) *pause* and notice the urge without doing anything about it; (2) *relax* by taking a deep breath, slowly exhaling, and consciously imagining the stress draining from your body; (3) *reflect* on what you are experiencing by asking yourself, "What do I have an urge to do? What has happened when I have done similar things in the past? What is likely to happen if I do that now?"; and then (4) *decide* what you are going to do about the urge. Make a conscious choice instead of acting out in an automatic and unconscious way. When making the choice about what you are going to do, remind yourself you will be responsible for both the action and its consequences.

Remember: *Impulse control lives in the space between the urge and the action.* With this in mind, let's develop a Denial Management Plan for each of the denial patterns you commonly use.

Exercise 4–2: Managing the Second Denial Pattern You Selected

1. Write the *Personal Title* for the denial pattern you selected.

2. Write the *Personal Description* of the second denial pattern you selected.

3. Write a *Thought Statement*. When you're using this denial pattern what do you tend to think?

4. Write a *Thought Management Statement*. What is another way of thinking that will allow you to stop denial and

start identifying and solving your problems?

5. Write a *Feeling Statement*. When you're using this denial pattern what do you tend to feel?

6. Write a *Feeling Management Statement*. How could you manage those feelings in a way that will allow you to stop denial and start identifying and solving your problems?

7. Write an *Urge Statement*. When you're using this denial pattern what do you have an urge to do?

8. Write an *Urge Management Statement*. How could you manage the urge by doing something that will help you stop denial and start identifying and solving your problems?

9. Write a *Behavior Statement*. When you're using this denial pattern what to you usually do?

10. Write a *Behavior Management Statement*. What else could you do that would help you stop denial and start identifying and solving your problems?

11. Write a *Social Reaction Statement*. When you're using this denial pattern how do other people usually react?

12. Write a *Social Reaction Management Statement*. How could you invite people to react to you in a way that would help you stop denial and start identifying and solving your problems?

Write these statements for each of the three denial patterns the client selected. Then move to the next part of the exercise to bring all the information together.

Exercise 4–4: Bringing Your Denial Management Skills Together

In this exercise, our job is to bring all of this information together so you can develop some concrete ways to recognize and manage your denial when it gets turned on. Take a sheet of paper and divide it in two columns.

1. In the first column, make a combined list of all the thoughts associated with your three denial patterns.

2. In the second column, make a list of the new ways of thinking that could stop your denial.

3. In the first column, below the list of thoughts, make a combined list of all the feelings that are associated with the three denial patterns you selected.

4. In the second column, below the list of new ways of think-

ing, make a combined list of all new feeling management strategies that could help you stop denial.

5. In the first column, below the list of feelings, make a combined list of all the urges associated with the three denial patterns you selected.

6. In the second column, below the new feeling management strategies, make a combined list of all the new ways of managing those urges that could help you stop denial.

7. In the first column, below the list of urges, make a combined list of all the self-defeating behaviors associated with the three denial patterns you selected.

8. In the second column, make a combined list of all the new ways of behaving that could help you stop denial.

9. In the first column, below make a combined list of all the ways that invite others to become part of your three denial patterns.

10. In the second column, below make a combined list of all the new ways you could invite others to help you stop your denial.

11. After reviewing all the information you organized, what are the three most important things you could do that would help you stop using denial and to start identifying and solving your problems?

Exercise #5: Stopping Denial as You Think about Your Problems

This exercise will test your ability to recognize and manage your own denial as you think and talk about the problems that caused you to seek help. First, you will be asked to describe the problems that caused you to seek help. Then you will be asked to look at the relationship between your problems, your alcohol and drug use, and the potential consequences—both good and bad—of continuing to use alcohol or other drugs. You will then be asked to tie all this information together in your mind, look at the big picture of what is happening at this moment in your life, and make a hard decision about what you want to do about your problems. At each step in this process, you will be asked to notice if you were able to recognize and stop your denial when it was turned on.

In this exercise you will start applying your new denial management skills to your problems. This isn't easy because you will be asked to think and talk about serious and painful problems. Even though you start this exercise intending to be honest, you may find that your denial gets activated. Whenever you become aware that you are using denial, you can turn it off by pausing, relaxing, reflecting, and deciding.

Pause and notice that you are using denial. Just notice it—don't do anything about it. *Relax* by taking a deep breath, slowly exhaling, and consciously imagining the stress drain from your body. *Reflect* on what you are experiencing by asking yourself, "Do I really want to keep using denial, or do I want to look at what is really going on so I can decide what I want to do about it? *Decide* whether or not you will keep using denial or not. When making this choice, remind yourself that you will be responsible for the consequences.

We will use a procedure called a Denial Check to help you learn how to recognize and stop denial when it occurs. At the end of each exercise, or whenever I think you might be using denial, I'll call a time-out and complete the two-part denial check by asking you two questions: (1) What denial patterns did you use during this part of the exercise? Complete the two-part denial check below. (2) When did you notice you were using denial?

On the next page is a Denial Self-Monitoring Form that can be used between sessions to do Denial Checks. (This form is also reproduced in Appendix #1.)

Once you learn to recognize denial as you are using it, you will have a chance to practice stopping it. Finally you will learn to recognize the urge to use denial, which gives us the power to look at the truth without ever using denial.

Exercise 5–1: The Problems that Caused You to Seek Help

1. Let's make a list of the three most important problems that caused you to seek help at this time? A *problem title* is a word or a short phrase that is easy to remember. A *problem*

description is a sentence or short paragraph that describes what the problem is.

2. Complete the two-part denial check using the Denial Self-Monitoring Form. (See Appendix #1.)

Part 1: What denial patterns did you use during this part of the exercise? Check as many as needed.

☐ 1. Avoidance: "I'll talk about anything but my real problems!"

☐ 2. Absolute Denial: "No, not me, I don't have problems!"

☐ 3. Minimizing: "My problems aren't that bad!"

☐ 4. Rationalizing: "If I can find good enough reasons for my problems, I won't have to deal with them!"

☐ 5. Blaming: "If I can prove that my problems are not my fault, I won't have to deal with them!"

☐ 6. Comparing: "Showing that others are worse than me proves that I don't have serious problems!"

☐ 7. Compliance: "I'll pretend to do what you want If you'll leave me alone!"

☐ 8. Manipulating: "I'll only admit that I have problems if you agree to solve them for me"

☐ 9. Flight into Health: "Feeling better means that I'm cured!"

☐ 10. Recovery by Fear: "Being scared of my problems will make them go away!"

☐ 11. Strategic Hopelessness: "Since nothing works, I don't have to try!"

☐ 12. Democratic Disease State: "I have the right to destroy myself and no one has the right to stop me!"

Part 2: When did you notice you were using denial?

A. Not until after completing this part of the exercise and reading my answers.

B. While I was answering the questions.

C. I noticed the urge to start using denial before I started to answer the question, but I ended up using denial when I answered the questions anyway.

D. I noticed the urge to start using denial before I started to answer the question, so I stopped my denial and answered the questions honestly.

Mini-Education Session: As people start to learn denial management they program through a sequence of stages in their ability to recognize denial that goes like this:

Stage 1: I didn't recognize my denial until after completing this part of the exercise and reviewing my answers.

Stage 2: I recognized my denial while I was answering the questions.

Stage 3: I noticed the urge to start using denial before I started to answer the question, but I ended up using denial when I answered the questions anyway.

Stage 4: I noticed the urge to start using denial before I started to answer the question, and so I stopped my denial and answered the questions honestly.

Exercise 5–2: The Relationship of Your Problems to Alcohol and Other Drugs

Now let's explore the relationship between your problems and your use of alcohol and other drugs. To do this, take a separate sheet of paper for each problem on the problem list and fold the paper like a letter creating three sections—a top, a middle, and a bottom section. In the first section write the problem title and description.

At the top of the second section write the question, "What is the relationship between this problem and my use of alcohol or other drugs?" Before writing the answer to this question think about the following clarifying questions: Did using alcohol or other drugs cause this problem? (In other words, would you have this problem if you never used alcohol or other drugs?) Did using alcohol or other drugs make this problem worse than it would have been if you hadn't been using? Did you use alcohol or other drugs to deal with stress or pain caused by this problem?

4. Complete the two-part denial check using the Denial Self-Monitoring Form. (See Appendix #1.)

Exercise 5–3: The Consequences of Continued Alcohol or Drug Use

Now let's go back to the first problem on your problem list. What is the title of that problem? What is the description of that problem?

1. How could continuing to use alcohol or other drugs help you solve this problem or make it better?

2. How could continuing to use alcohol or other drugs prevent you from solving this problem or make it worse?

3. What is the best thing that could happen to this problem if you keep using?

4. What is the worst thing that could happen to this problem if you keep using?

5. What is the most likely thing that will happen to this problem if you keep using?

6. Complete the two-part denial check using the Denial Self-Monitoring Form. (See Appendix #1.)

Complete the above process for the other problems on the problem list.

Exercise 5–4: Pulling It All Together

The purpose of this exercise is to help you pull together the information from the previous three exercises so you can look at the big picture of what is happening to you as a result of your alcohol or drug use and make decisions about what you want to do.

Take a sheet of paper and divide it into three columns.

1. Review the problems that caused you to seek treatment and write those problems in Column #1: Presenting Problems.

2. In Column #2, describe how each problem is related to your use of alcohol and other drugs and write that.

3. In Column #3, list the best, worst, and most likely things that could happen as a result of each problem if you continue to use alcohol or other drugs.

On the next page is a sample of the three-column worksheet reproduced from *The Denial Management Counseling Workbook.*

4. Review the information you summarized on the previous table. Try to connect with what this information means to you.

5. What do you think will happen to your problems if you keep using alcohol or other drugs? Explain your answer.

6. Do you think that if you stop using alcohol and drugs, at least for a while, things might start getting better? Explain your answer.

7. Do you believe it is in your best interest to stop using alcohol and drugs, at least for a while? Explain your answer.

8. Are you willing to make a commitment to abstain from alcohol and other drugs? Explain your answer.

9. Are you willing to develop an Abstinence Plan that will help you stay away from alcohol and other drugs while working to solve your problems? Explain your answer.

10. Are you willing to be accountable for your decision not

1. Presenting Problems:	2. Relationship to Alcohol or Drug Use:	3. Consequences of Continued Use:
What are the presenting problems that caused you to seek treatment at this time?	How is each presenting problem related to your use of alcohol or drugs?	What will happen to your ability to solve this problem if you don't stop using alcohol and drugs?
Problem #1:		Best:
		Worst:
		Most likely:

to use alcohol or other drugs by agreeing to participate in an alcohol and drug screening program? Explain your answer.

11. Are you willing to start a treatment program that can help you implement your abstinence plan? Explain your answer.

12. Complete the two-part denial check using the Denial Self-Monitoring Form. (See Appendix #1.)

Exercise #6: Stopping Denial as You Think about Your Life History

In this exercise you will be asked to review the important things that have happened to you in the course of your life and think about how alcohol and drugs were related to each of the key life events. At each step in this process, you will be asked to notice if you were able to recognize and stop your denial when it was turned on.

1. Developing the Life History: Your first job is to develop a life and addiction history. Take a sheet of paper and divide it into two columns. At the top of the first column write *Significant Life Events.* At the top of the second column write *Alcohol and Drug Use Pattern.*

In Column #1, briefly describe the sequence of significant life events that you experienced from birth until now: use brief bullet points that capture the essence of each event. You should be able to summarize your entire life history in a couple of pages.

Note: Don't ask about alcohol or drug use. If information is volunteered make note of it, but treat it lightly.

2. Developing the Alcohol and Other Drug (AOD) History: Go to Column #2 and describe your pattern of alcohol and drug use during each phase of the lifeline: What substances did you use during this period of your life? How much did you use? How often did you use? What did you want to get out of using alcohol or drugs? What fears did you have about using alcohol or drugs? What actually happened as a result of your alcohol and drug use?

A sample of the two-column life and addiction history is presented below.

3. What did you want alcohol or drugs to allow you to do that you couldn't do without them?

4. Did your alcohol and drug use get you what you wanted? Explain your answer.

1. Significant Life Events:	2. Alcohol and Drug Use Pattern:
Describe the sequence of significant life events: Use brief bullet points that capture the essence of each event. You should be able to summarize the entire life history of the client by reviewing the events in Column #1. Don't ask about alcohol or drug use. If information is volunteered make note of it, but treat it lightly.	Describe the pattern of alcohol and drug use during each phase of the lifeline. Questions: (1) What substances did you use? (2) How much did you use? (3) How often did you use? (4) What did you want to get out of using alcohol or drugs? 5) What fears did you have about using alcohol or drugs? (6) What actually happened as a result of your alcohol and drug use?
Life Event #__	

5. What did you want alcohol or drugs to allow you to cope with or escape from that you couldn't when not using?

6. Did your alcohol and drug use give you the escape or coping skills you wanted? Explain your answer.

7. After reviewing your history, what were the benefits and disadvantages that alcohol and drugs brought to your life? Take a separate sheet of paper and list the benefits in the first column and the disadvantages in the second column.

Benefits of Alcohol and Drug Use	Disadvantages of Alcohol and Drug Use
1.	1.
2.	2.
3.	3.

8. What are the three most important things you learned about yourself by completing your history of significant life events and the relationship of those events to your alcohol and drug use?

9. Complete the two part-denial check using the Denial Self-Monitoring Form. (See Appendix #1.)

Exercise #7: Stopping Denial as You Think about Your Addiction Symptoms

In this exercise you will review the common symptoms of substance abuse and dependence and be asked to decide if each symptom applies to you. You will then be able to tie all your answers together to see if you meet medical criteria for substance abuse or dependence or if you are at high risk of developing it. At each step in this process, you will be asked to notice if you were able to recognize and stop your denial when it was turned on.

1. Do you use alcohol more than twice a week? Do you consider that a problem? Explain.

2. On the days when you use alcohol, do you usually have three or more drinks? Do you consider that a problem? Explain.

3. Do you use nonprescription drugs from time to time? Do you consider that a problem? Explain.

4. Do you use prescription drugs that change your mood or personality? Do you consider that a problem? Explain.

5. Do you sometimes use more than the amount prescribed? Do you consider that a problem? Explain.

6. Do you get intoxicated on alcohol or drugs more than twice a year? (You're intoxicated if you use so much that you can't function safely or normally; or if other people think you can't function safely or normally.) Do you consider that a problem? Explain.

7. When you're not using alcohol or drugs, do you ever put yourself in situations that raise your risk of getting hurt or having problems? Do you consider that a problem? Explain.

8. Have you ever felt you should cut down on your drinking or drug use? Do you consider that a problem? Explain.

9. Have other people ever criticized your drinking or drug use, or been annoyed by it? Do you consider that a problem? Explain.

10. Have you ever felt bad or guilty about your drinking or drug use? Do you consider that a problem? Explain.

11. Have you ever done things while you were using alcohol or drugs that you regretted or that made you feel guilty or ashamed? Do you consider that a problem? Explain.

12. Have you ever used alcohol or drugs first thing in the morning to feel better, or to get rid of a hangover? Do you consider that a problem? Explain.

13. Have you ever thought you might have a problem with your drinking or drug use? Do you consider that a problem? Explain.

14. Have you ever used alcohol or drugs in larger quantities than you intended? (For example, have you ever used more than you wanted to or could afford to?) Do you consider that a problem? Explain.

15. Have you ever used alcohol or drugs more often than you intended? (For example, have you ever planned not to use that day but done it anyway?) Do you consider that a problem? Explain.

16. Have you ever used alcohol or drugs for longer periods of time than you intended? (In other words, have you ever not been able to stop when you planned to?) Do you consider that a problem? Explain.

17. Have you ever had a desire to cut down or control your use?

18. Have you ever tried to cut down or control your use? Do you consider that a problem? Explain.

19. Do you spend a lot of time getting ready to use alcohol or drugs, using, or recovering from using? Do you consider that a problem? Explain.

20. Have you ever failed to meet a major life responsibility because you were intoxicated, hung over, or in withdrawal (having discomfort because you were no longer using)? Do you consider that a problem? Explain.

21. Have you given up any work, social, or recreational activities because of alcohol or drug use? Do you consider that a problem? Explain.

22. Have you had any physical, psychological, or social problems that were caused by, or made worse by, your alcohol or drug use? Do you consider that a problem? Explain.

23. Have you ever continued to use alcohol or drugs even though you knew they were causing physical, psychological, or social problems, or making those problems worse? Do you consider that a problem? Explain.

24. Did your tolerance (your ability to use a lot of alcohol and drugs without feeling intoxicated) increase after you started to use? Do you consider that a problem? Explain.

25. Do you ever get physically uncomfortable or sick the day after using alcohol or drugs? Do you consider that a problem? Explain.

26. Have you ever used alcohol or drugs to keep you from getting sick the next day or to make a hangover go away? Do you consider that a problem? Explain.

27. When you use alcohol or drugs, what do you want those substances to do for you that you believe you can't do without them?

28. When you use alcohol or drugs, what do you want those

substances to help you escape from that you believe you can't escape without them?

Finding Out What Your Answers Mean

To find out what the answers to the questions mean, let's complete the following steps:

First, count how many times the client answered "yes" to Questions 1–13 and write that number down.

Second, count how many times the client answered "yes" to Questions 14–26 and write that number down.

If you answered "no" to all of the questions, you are probably at *Low Risk of Addiction.*

If you answered "yes" to three or more of Questions I–13 and "no" to all of the remaining questions, you are probably at *High Risk of Addiction.*

If you answered "yes" to more than three of Questions I–13 and "yes" to between three and six of Questions 14–26, you are probably in the *Early Stages of Addiction.*

If you answered "yes" to more than three of Questions 1–13 and "yes" to between six and nine of Questions 14–26, you are probably in the *Middle Stages of Addiction.*

If you answered "yes" to more than three of Questions I–13 and "yes" to more than nine of Questions 14–26, you are probably in the *Late Stages of Addiction.*

You are probably dependent on alcohol or drugs if you believe that (1) alcohol and drugs can do things for you that you can't do without those substances, or (2) alcohol and drugs can help you cope with things that you can't cope with unless you're using. Only people who are dependent on alcohol or drugs expect these substances to do things for them that they can't do without them.

Complete the two-part denial check using the Denial Self-Monitoring Form. (See Appendix #1.)

Exercise #8: Stopping Denial as You Decide What to Do Next

In this exercise you will be asked to decide what you are going to do next. You can decide to stay in denial and pretend your problems don't exist, or you can decide to recognize your problems and enter appropriate treatment so you can learn to effectively manage your alcohol and drug problems and get your life back on track.

1. What are the problems that caused you to seek help?
2. How is your alcohol and other drug use related to those problems?
3. Do you believe you can successfully deal with those problems if you stopped using alcohol and other drugs, at least for a limited period of time? Explain your answer.
4. Are you willing to make a commitment to get the help you need to stop using alcohol and other drugs? Explain your answer.
5. Complete the two-part denial check using the Denial Self-Monitoring Form. (See Appendix #1.)

Exercise #9: Evaluating Your Denial Management Skills

In this exercise you will evaluate how well you learned the skills needed to recognize and manage your denial. Learning to identify and manage your denial is not easy, but it is a necessary first step in learning how to recover from serious alcohol and drug problems. Learning to manage your denial will require hard work and a willingness to use each exercise in this workbook as a tool for self-examination and self-change. It will also require you to apply the skills while looking at the problems that forced you into treatment, examining your life and addiction history, and evaluating the addiction symptoms you have experienced. *You can recover.* Learning how to manage your denial will help.

The ultimate test of whether you have benefited from this training will be your ability to identify and stop your denial and start identifying and solving your problems. This evaluation will help you identify your areas of strength and weakness so you will be able to improve your overall skill at managing your denial.

I'm going to ask you a series of questions to help you evaluate your level of skill before completing these exercises and your current level of skill after completing these exercises.

1. What did you want from completing these exercises?
2. Did you get what you wanted? Explain your answer:
3. What are the most important things you learned about yourself by completing this workbook?
4. What will you do differently as a result of completing this workbook?
5. The following questions will help you rate your skills at managing denial.

Skill #1: Understanding Denial as a Part of the Human Condition: I am able to explain why denial is a normal part of the human condition (Exercise #1).

Skill #2: Understanding the Principles of Denial Management: I am able to explain the basic principles of denial management (Exercise #2).

Skill #3: Recognizing Your Denial: I know the denial patterns that I tend to use most frequently and can recognize when these denial patterns get turned on.

Skill #4: Managing Your Denial: I can stop my denial quickly when it occurs and focus on identifying and solving my problems.

Skill #5: Stopping Denial as You Think about Your Problems: I can stop using denial as I think about the problems that caused me to get help, how those problems are related to alcohol and other drug use, and what will probably happen if I keep using alcohol or other drugs.

Skill #6: Stopping Denial as You Think about Your Life History: I can stop using denial as I think about my history of significant life events and how my use of alcohol or other drugs is related to those events.

Skill #7: Stopping Denial as You Think about Your Addiction Symptoms: I am able to stop denial as I review the symptoms of addiction that apply to me.

Skill #8: Stopping Denial as You Decide What to Do Next: I can stop using denial as I think about what I need to do next to deal with my alcohol and drug problems.

Overall Skill at Managing High-Risk Situations: How would you rate the changes in your overall ability to recognize and stop denial quickly and then refocus on identifying and solving your problems? Why did you rate your changes in skill levels this way?

2–5: Denial Self-Management Training (DSMT)

Denial Self-Management Training (DSMT) is **a structured psychoeducational program** for clients exhibiting severe denial. This program can be offered in a variety of settings and levels of care. DSMT is most commonly used in residential rehabilitation, day treatment, or intensive outpatient programs. One of the keys to the success of DSMT programs is their intensity. The program needs to be offered as an intensive course that immerges clients in a new approach to managing their pain and problems.

Therapeutic Slippage: Clients tend to forget what they learned and lose touch with the intense feelings that were generated in previous sessions. This is called therapeutic slippage. Slippage occurs because clients return to an environment that activates their denial and creates the urge to use self-defeating behaviors. Once these old defensive ways of thinking and acting are activated, the clients entire state of consciousness can shift and their old self-reinforcing symptom cycle can be reactivated. As a result, when clients come for their next session much of the therapeutic gain that was observed in the previous session is lost.

Ways to Minimize Therapeutic Slippage: There are several ways to minimize the amount of therapeutic slippage that occurs between sessions.

The first way to minimize therapeutic slippage is to schedule longer sessions and closer together. Holding DSMT class sessions of three hours each scheduled on Monday, Wednesday, and Friday evenings, for example, will produce less slippage in between sessions than scheduling 90-minute sessions once per week.

The second way to minimize therapeutic slippage is to structure each class session to produce a maximum amount of therapeutic change. The greater the change in each session, the less slippage will occur before the next session. This means structuring each class session with a skill-oriented presentation that is reinforced by experiential exercises that force the client to use the skills they are learning.

The third way to minimize therapeutic slippage is to give homework assignments that reinforce the material covered in the session. These homework assignments can include attendance at self-help groups, structured self-monitoring and self-change exercises, interviewing exercises, and reading and journaling assignments.

DSMT Is Most Effective with Clients Who Have Strong, Persistent Denial, and Resistance. Clients who are not locked into a pattern of strong denial can become angry and resentful by being forced to attend a DSMT program. This anger can actually activate denial. Clients who are not in strong denial should be assigned to programs that will allow them to directly address the motivational crisis and target problems they are capable of identifying.

All clients, of course, will exhibit some denial as they identify and clarify painful problems. When denial surfaces, the therapist should use the Denial Management Interactional Process to expose and defuse the denial process and focus the client once again on the core problem. It is only when the client's denial occurs so frequently and is so severe that it prevents the completion of a routine diagnostic or treatment procedure that a formal, structured DSMT program should be considered.

Some Clients Have Minimal Denial or Good Denial Self-Management Skills and Will Not Benefit from Denial Self-Management Training. It is important to remember that not all clients are suffering from severe denial. Some clients have had a motivational crisis that has interrupted their denial. They are willing and able to see the truth. Many clients who appear to be in severe denial are merely operating based on misinformation. Once they learn about their target disorder and are guided through no-nonsense assessment procedures the accurate information coupled with solid self-assessment skills motivate the client to move ahead into problem solving. Still other clients have been in treatment before and have learned to identify and manage their denial.

Using DSMT as a Blanket Intervention for All Clients Will

Have Limited Effectiveness. It is also important to remember that a good way to create denial is to pre-judge a client, try to impose your judgment, and when the client refuses to accept the false pre-judgment accuse them of being in denial. "One size does not fit all clients." Clients tend to respond in a motivated manner when the clinical approach of the therapist matches the nature and severity of their presenting problems and is compatible with their personality style. Because of this, the key to successful treatment is to match clients to appropriate clinical styles and treatment interventions.

To Be Effective DSMT Must Be Matched to Clients Who Can Benefit from It. There is no simplistic, universal solution to the problem of addictive and mental health disorders. As a result there is no single magic bullet that will work effectively with these complex biopsychosocial disorders. Denial self-management training is not a universal cure-all, but it can work effectively with clients who exhibit severe denial and resistance.

DSMT Admission Criteria

One of the important keys to successful treatment outcome is patient treatment matching. As mentioned earlier, denial management principles work best with clients who are exhibiting severe denial and treatment resistance that is interfering with their ability to honestly face serious problems and take the necessary steps to deal effectively with those problems.

DSMT Admission Criteria:

1. Substance-related motivational crisis
2. Ability to be abstinent and stable in sessions
3. Strong denial of substance abuse
4. Strong resistance to treatment
5. Willingness to participate in DSMT process

We can develop a set of five criteria that help you decide which clients could benefit from a central focus on MRC methods.

1. *The client has a substance-related motivational crisis:* Understanding the concept of a motivational crisis is critical

to be able to work effectively with clients who are exhibiting severe denial and treatment resistance. Start by examining the core crisis.

Webster's Third New International Dictionary, Unabridged, proposes six possible definitions for the word crisis: (1) A turning point for better or worse in an acute disease or fever; (2) an emotionally significant event or radical change of status in a person's life; (3) the point in time when it is decided whether an affair or course of action should proceed, be modified, or terminate; (4) a decisive moment; a turning point; (5) an unstable state of affairs in which a decisive change is impending; (6) a psychological or social condition characterized by unusual instability caused by excessive stress that either endangers or is felt to endanger the continuity of the individual or his group.

By reading these definitions it becomes clear that a crisis is a situation or an event that represents *a turning point* for better or worse in a person's life. The crisis situation is emotionally significant to the person experiencing it because *it forces the person to make a decision.*

The crisis brings a sequence of events or a course of action to a climax or conclusion by forcing one of three decisions. (1) I can continue things as they are hoping for the best; (2) I change my course of action in life while continuing to pursue the same or similar goals; or (3) I can end or terminate the pursuit of a specific goal and totally disengage from any course of action related to achieving that goal. A crisis, therefore is, a decisive moment or a turning point in a person's life when an unstable state of affairs is forcing a conscious decision.

Most crises are biopsychosocial in nature. At the moment of crisis people are experiencing very high levels of biological stress that can impair their judgment, impulse control, and ability to take effective action. At some level the person knows that in the midst of crisis they cannot make a good decision. Yet there is a need to decide and act immediately because the situation represents an emergency that poses a real and present danger to the person, people they love and care about, or their way of life. As a result, a true crisis represents a survival threat. When faced with a survival threat the entire biopsychological organism prepares for lifesaving action and begins to mobilize their social resources in order to help them survive.

When I was a new counselor I found an interesting quote on the back of a Borax bleach box. The quote, printed beneath a picture of the twenty-mule train passing a bleached skeleton of a cow as it was crossing the desert, went something like this: *"There are many bleached bones on the battlefield of decision, because at the moment of choice many people pause and die with the waiting."*

This is the problem with a crisis. The crisis can motivate a change in behavior either for better or worse. The crisis can also reinforce the belief that the best course of action is to keep doing what they have been doing that created the problem.

Many times people will use a crisis to reinforce a set of self-defeating beliefs such as, "I am right! Everyone else is wrong! Things should be working better! My only option is to keep doing what I know how to do while hoping for a better outcome." When the crisis produces this response, the person is said to be in denial. Their mental processes in the moment of crisis are distorted, and they are using bad judgment and are often out of control because they cannot control their impulses to act in a responsible manner.

So consider the need for denial management any time you see a person in a crisis marked by denial and resistance.

2. The client has the ability to be abstinent and stable in sessions: Many substance abusers are suffering from severe intoxication or withdrawal when the motivational crisis hits. They are, in essence, incapacitated by the effects of alcohol or drugs. They are incapable of making and implementing a rational decision. Before Denial Self-Management Training can be effective the person must be stabilized, and this may require the completion of a program of alcohol and drug detoxification. The Denial Management Interactional Process can be helpful to temporarily interrupt denial and delusional thinking and motivate the person in that moment to seek help. It is important to remember, however, that when people are under the influence of alcohol or drugs or experiencing alcohol or drug withdrawal their mental process are not stable. They are volatile and subject to change at a moment's notice.

The general rule is to get people who are intoxicated or in withdrawal into an adequately controlled environment as quickly as possible when the motivational crisis forces them to take action. A period of even several hours can allow the person to lapse back into believing that drinking and drugging is their best course of action. The window of opportunity for the intervention will then pass.

Once the person is detoxified and has a stable mental status, they can benefit from a formal structured denial self-management training program.

3. The client has strong denial of substance abuse: Clients who are in strong denial of their substance abuse tend to benefit most from denial self-management training (DSMT). It's helpful to ask the following questions: Does the client have a motivational crisis that is clearly related to the use or abuse of alcohol or other drugs? Is there clear evidence of the relationship? Has that evidence been presented to the client? Does the client have an accurate understanding of substance use disorders? In spite this, does the client still persist in their belief that they don't have a serious alcohol or drug problem? If the answer to these questions is yes, you have a client who is well-suited for DSMT.

4. The client has strong resistance to treatment: Clients who are initially resistant to treatment also make good candidates for DSMT. It is important to remember that resistant clients are generally motivated by the threat of adverse consequences. Their primary goal is not to make meaningful long-term changes in their lives. Their primary goal is to do the minimum necessary to avoid the adverse consequences. They are willing to comply with treatment, but they will do so reluctantly.

Resistant clients require a structured program with clearly learning objectives, structured behavioral guidelines for participation, and clear enforceable consequences for failure to comply. If the program is then structured so that the client is forced to participate in activities that produce insight into the problem and a corrective emotional experience, the client can move from *external motivation* directed at avoiding an undesirable adverse consequence to an *internal motivation* directed at making changes they perceive are of personal value.

It is important to remember that the initial level of self-motivation is not a significant predictor of the outcome of substance-abuse treatment. The type and duration of treatment is a much more powerful predictor. Remember the AA slogan: "Bring the body and the mind will follow." In the initial phase of treatment with an involuntary referral, the goal is to get compliance with a structured treatment process that forces the client to go through the motions of effective problem identification and problem solving and forces them to expose and deal with the denial patterns that are preventing them from recognizing and dealing effectively with their problems. This leads us to the final criteria.

5. The client has a willingness to comply with the DSMT process: The client must be willing to comply with the DSMT process. They don't have to want to do it. They don't have to like it. They just have to go through the process without being disruptive.

This compliance, however, means more than just bringing the body. A willingness to comply can be translated into several behavioral indicators. First, the clients have to agree to actively participate in the education and discussion process. They must also agree not to disrupt sessions. The clients need to clearly understand that they will be expected to participate in class sessions, they will be tested on what they have learned, and they will be asked to develop a plan for how they are going to use what they are learning to deal effectively with their alcohol or drug problem and improve the quality of their lives.

This willingness to comply means clients have to agree to abstain from alcohol and drugs during the course of the program. The decision often needs to be enforced by random alcohol and drug testing. The program also needs to have a clear, corrective discipline process that is consistently used whenever a client fails to comply with behavioral guidelines.

The Denial Self-Management Training (DSMT) Program

Denial Self-Management Training (DSMT) Program	
Session 1: Understanding Denial • The dynamics of denial and the principles of denial management	**Session 6: Denial Pattern Management** • Managing Irrational thoughts, intense feelings and emotions, and self-defeating behaviors related to each pattern
Session 2: Big Five Denial Patterns • Avoidance, Absolute Denial, Minimizing, Rationalizing, and Blaming	**Session 7: Abstinence and Treatment Contract** • Link presenting problems to substance-use self-monitoring for denial
Session 3: Small Seven Denial Patterns • Comparison, Manipulating, Scaring Myself Into Recovery, Compliance, Flight into Health, Diagnosis of Self as Beyond Help, The Democratic Disease State.	**Session 8: Brief Life and Addiction History** • Analyze key life events and their relationship to substance use while self-monitoring for denial
Session 4: Denial Self-Assessment • Denial Pattern Checklist, Personal Denial Patterns and Management Strategies	**Session 9: Addiction Symptom Review** • Analyze an addiction symptoms checklist while self-monitoring for denial
Session 5: Denial Pattern Analysis • Identify the Thought, Feelings, Behaviors, and social reactions related to each denial pattern	**Session 10: Recovery Plan** • Develop a recovery plan to support self-monitoring of denial

Denial Self-Management Training (DSMT) Program is an intensive course that teaches clients how to recognize and manage their own denial. A typical DSMT program consists of twelve sessions that are two or three hours in duration. The sessions follow a logical sequence in which the basic information about denial and denial management is presented and participants complete a sequence of addiction evaluation exercises that give them an opportunity to recognize and consciously manage their denial when it is activated.

Each class session typically includes an educational presentation, a journaling or self-evaluation exercise, small group exercises, a large group discussion, a closure exercise, and a homework assignment to prepare for the next class. A typical class session is two to three hours long and includes of 15 to 20 persons. Let's review a session-by-session description of a typical Denial Self-Management Training Program.

Session 1: Understanding Denial

This session explains *The Dynamics of Denial* and *The Basic Principles of Denial Management.*

Participants write a list of their presenting problems (i.e., the problems that caused them to be referred into the program). Each participant finds a partner and discusses their presenting problems while consciously monitoring their thoughts and feelings. They then share what they were thinking and feeling as they were telling their partner about their presenting problems. The entire class then discusses what was learned by the exercise.

The goal of this exercise is to help participants notice that when they are asked to think about or talk about the problems that caused them to be referred into treatment two things happen: First, an inner conflict is activated (One part of them saying, "I don't have any problems!" and another part of them saying, "Yes, you do!") Second, they experience unpleasant feelings and emotions including fear, anger, shame, guilt, and pain which they are reluctant to talk about.

Participants are given the assignment to read Handout #1: The Big Five Denial Patterns and to write a story about someone who used one of the Big Five denial patterns to try to avoid dealing with a serious problem.

Participants end the session by completing a closure exercise by discussing with their partner or in a small group of six to eight people the most important thing they learned about themselves in this session and what they plan to do differently as a result of what they learned.

Session 2: The Big Five Denial Patterns

This session explains the Big Five denial patterns (Avoidance, Absolute Denial, Minimizing, Rationalizing, and Blaming). Each participant is given time to review and improve his or her homework assignment (Write a story about someone who used one of the Big Five denial patterns to try to avoid dealing with a serious problem). The class is divided into small groups of six to eight people, and each person is asked to take two minutes to tell the story they just wrote down. Then each person is asked to write down the most important thing he or she learned by doing the exercise (listening to the lecture on the denial patterns, writing and telling the story, and listening to the stories of others). The group leader is asked to make a list of the most important things group members learned. The group leaders then report to the group summarizing the most important things the group members learned. Participants are given the assignment to read Handout #2: The Small Seven Denial Patterns and to prepare a story about someone they know who used one of the Small Seven Denial Patterns to try to avoid dealing with a serious problem.

Participants end the session by completing a closure exercise by discussing in their small group the most important thing they learned about themselves in this session and what they plan to do differently as a result of what they learned.

Session 3: The Small Seven Denial Patterns

This session explains the Small Seven Denial Patterns (Comparison, Compliance, Manipulating, Flight into Health, Recovery by Fear, Strategic Hopelessness, Democratic Disease State). Each participant is given time to review and improve his or her homework assignment (Write a story of a time when someone they know, other than themselves, used one or more of the Small Seven denial patterns to try to avoid dealing with a serious problem). The class is divided into small groups of six to eight people, and each person is asked to take two minutes to tell their story. Then each person is asked to write down the most important thing he or she learned by doing the exercise (listening to the lecture on the denial patterns, writing and telling the story, and listening to the stories of others). The group leader is asked to make a list of the most important things group members learned. The group leaders then report to the group summarizing the most important things the group members learned. Participants are given the assignment to read Handout #3: The Denial Pattern Checklist.

Participants end the session by completing a closure exercise by discussing in their small group the most important thing they learned about themselves in this session and what they plan to do differently as a result of what they learned.

Session 4: Denial Self-Assessment

In this session participants read The Denial Pattern Checklist out loud in their small groups, identify the three primary denial patterns they tend to use most often, and write both a personal description and a denial management plan for each of the three denial patterns. They then present their personal descriptions and denial management strategies to their small group.

Participants end the session by completing a closure exercise by discussing in their small group the most important thing they learned about themselves in this session and what they plan to do differently as a result of what they learned.

Session 5: Denial Pattern Analysis

In this session participants review the three personal denial patterns and identify the thoughts, feelings, behaviors, and social reactions that are related to each denial pattern.

Participants end the session by completing a closure exercise by discussing in their small group the most important thing they learned about themselves in this session and what they plan to do differently as a result of what they learned.

Session 6: Denial Pattern Management

In this session participants learn how to develop a denial management plan for each of their primary denial patterns. This denial management plan includes learning how to challenge the irrational thoughts, manage the intense feelings, and stop the self-defeating behaviors related to each denial pattern. They also learn how to involve significant others in recognizing and effectively managing denial when it is activated.

Participants end the session by completing a closure exercise by discussing in their small group the most important thing they learned about themselves in this session and what they plan to do differently as a result of what they learned.

Session 7: Abstinence and Treatment Contract

This session teaches participants how to link presenting problems to substance use while self-monitoring for denial. This includes developing a list of presenting problems that motivated them to enter treatment, identifying the relationship of each presenting problem to alcohol or drug use, projecting the logical consequences of continued substance use on their ability to solve each problem, and making a commitment to abstain for the duration of the assessment process while self-monitoring for denial and consciously managing the denial patterns that are activated.

Participants end the session by completing a closure exercise by discussing in their small group the most important thing they learned about themselves in this session and what they plan to do differently as a result of what they learned.

Session 8: Brief Life and Addiction History

This session teaches participants how to analyze key life events while self-monitoring for denial. This includes developing a list of key life events and examining the role the substance use played in each major life event while self-monitoring for denial and consciously managing the denial patterns that are activated.

Participants end the session by completing a closure exercise by discussing in their small group the most important thing they learned about themselves in this session and what they plan to do differently as a result of what they learned.

Session 9: Addiction Symptom Review

This session teaches clients how to analyze an *Addiction Symptom Checklist* while self-monitoring for denial. This involves using a checklist to evaluate the severity of symptoms they are currently experiencing. The symptoms on the Addiction Symptom Checklist are reviewed in a brief lecture. Participants are asked to identify the addiction symptoms they have experienced, rate the frequency and severity of each symptom, and share their self-assessment with a partner and in their small group while self-monitoring for denial and consciously managing the denial patterns that are activated. Near the end of the session participants identify the denial patterns that were activated during this exercise and evaluate their ability to recognize and manage each denial pattern.

Participants end the session by completing a closure exercise by discussing in their small group the most important thing they learned about themselves in this session and what they plan to do differently as a result of what they learned.

Session 10: Recovery Plan

In this session participants develop a recovery plan while self-monitoring for denial. This includes developing a specific recovery plan for the next stage of their recovery while self-monitoring for denial and consciously managing the denial patterns that are activated. They present their recovery plan to their small group, and complete a closure exercise in which they report the most important thing they learned during the Denial Self-Management Course, what they plan to do differently as a result of what they learned, and receive final feedback from their small group.

Participants end the session by completing a closure exercise by discussing in their small group the most important thing they learned about themselves in this session and what they plan to do differently as a result of what they learned.

Part 3

Advanced Clinical Skills for Denial Management

This part of the book explains how to apply the intervention steps (steps 3–7) of the Denial Management Interactional Process to each of the twelve denial patterns. Be sure to read and understand the general principles of the Denial Management Interactional Process that were presented in the preceding section. This will give you the general overview of the process needed to understand each individual application.

The preparation steps (Focused Question and Active Listening) are the same for all denial patterns, so I won't repeat those two steps. We will assume that the clients have completed a focused interview that used active listening and that the denial pattern being discussed was such a problem that it had to be dealt with directly by using the intervention steps of the Denial Management Interactional Process.

Many steps of the process are nearly identical when applied to different denial patterns. To avoid unnecessary repetition of basic procedures, I'll describe the application of the Denial Management Interactional Process in detail for the first denial pattern (avoidance). From that point on I will only describe in detail applications of the process that vary significantly from one denial pattern to another. For procedures that are the same when applied to all denial patterns, you will be referred back to either the general description of the process in the previous section or to the detailed application for the avoidance denial pattern that follows.

Let's start with the first denial pattern—avoidance.

3-1: Avoidance

Most therapists begin to suspect that clients are using avoidance when they can't keep focused on important issues. Every time they try to use active listening to refocus their clients, they somehow end up discussing interesting but irrelevant aspects of the client's problem. Because focused questions and active listening have not worked, it's time to move on to the intervention steps of the Denial Management Interactional Process.

Identifying Avoidance

The first step is to identify avoidance.

Gut Reactions: Avoidance tends to produce the following gut reactions in most therapists: (1) a fascination with what the client is saying because clients are talking about things that are interesting and intriguing; (2) frustration because the clients keep going off the agenda and there is no time to deal with the core issues; and (3) anger because the client agrees to stay focused and then gets off track again.

Nonverbal Indicators: Clients using avoidance become intensely interested and emotionally excited when pursuing sidetracks. They seem bored or disinterested when talking about core issues and try to shift the session focus if they can.

Behavioral Goals: The behavioral goals of avoidance are to: (1) focus on interesting but irrelevant things, (2) avoid thinking or talking about their core problems, and (3) avoid the painful feelings related to their core problems.

Cognitive Themes and Self-Talk: The cognitive theme of avoidance is: "I'll talk about anything but the real problem!" The client will not explicitly make that statement but will refuse to focus on the core problem by changing the subject and refusing to answer questions directly.

Identifying the Mistaken Beliefs: The mistaken belief that motivates their avoidance is: "If I refuse to think or talk about the problem, it will go away."

Exposing Avoidance

To expose the avoidance denial pattern you can say, *"What I'm hearing you say is that you want to avoid the real issue by talking about something else. Is that correct?* This puts clients in a position where they have to notice what they are thinking and doing in the moment. It also focuses the session on the immediate here-and-now interaction between the therapist and the client. The closed question "Is that correct?" limits the client's responses to "yes" or "no." They need to either agree with you, disagree, or refuse to answer. Remember, clients who are using the avoidance pattern will try to avoid telling you whether or not they believe you are correct.

If clients agree with you, move on to Step 5: Educating about Avoidance. If clients don't agree, apologize for making a mistake and ask them to explain what they are doing. You can say, *"I'm sorry. I thought you were trying to avoid answering my question by changing the subject to other things. I guess I must be mistaken. May I ask you the question again?*

Clients with deeply entrenched avoidance patterns will begin answering the question and then try to lead you into another sidetrack. Let them lead you far enough away from the point so that their avoidance is obvious and undeniable. Then repeat the exposing statement by saying, *"What I'm hearing you say now is that you still want to avoid the real issue by talking about something else. Is that correct?"*

If clients deny using avoidance again the second time you expose it you can use this response: *"I'm sorry. I thought you were trying to avoid answering my question by changing the subject to other things. I guess I must be mistaken. Could you tell me what you are trying to do?*

Notice that the ending question, "Could you tell me what you are trying to do?" puts the responsibility on the client to stop, observe their own behavior, and tell you what they are trying to do. The procedure of stopping denial and inviting clients to use self-monitoring and self-reporting is the key to exposing any denial pattern.

Educating about Avoidance

The next step is to educate clients about avoidance by using five methods: (1) description, (2) education, (3) examples of others, (4) personal examples, and (5) stories and analogies. Let's look at these methods in more detail.

Description: You can describe Avoidance by saying, *"You seem to be answering my questions by using a denial pattern* *called avoidance. Do you know what avoidance is?"* This approach gives direct feedback to the client while immediately channeling the expected defensiveness into responding to the closed question, "Do you know what avoidance is? If the answer is "yes," ask, "Tell me what you think avoidance is." Then focus on clarifying and correcting the client's answer. If the answer is "no," go to the next step—education.

Education: You can say, *"Avoidance is a way of dealing with problems by refusing to think or talk about them by focusing on other things. People tend to use avoidance because they believe they can make their problems go away by refusing to think or talk about them."*

If the client gets upset or defensive, you can defuse the defensiveness by saying, *"I'm sorry I upset you. I was just trying to explain my understanding of what avoidance is. I didn't mean to upset you. What did I do or say that made you so upset?"*

Examples of Others: You can then ask clients for examples of other people who used avoidance: "Have you ever tried to talk with someone about a problem and they kept sidetracking you and refusing to answer your question directly?"

Personal Examples: Then you can ask for personal examples of avoidance by focusing on several past experiences that have already been resolved. This makes it easier for them to see how they are avoiding the current problem. You can say, *"Most people tend to use avoidance when they have a serious problem they don't want to deal with at the moment. Sometimes it's just easier to focus on other things for a little while and hope the problem goes away. Have you ever used avoidance to keep from thinking or talking about a problem you knew was serious? Tell me about it."*

Stories and Analogies: You can then tell clients a story or analogy about avoidance. As mentioned earlier, I like to use *The Story of Jake the Snake:*

Listening to you reminds me of a client I once treated named Jake. They called him Jake the Snake because he was so slippery. He was the best I've ever seen at using avoidance to keep from talking about his problems with alcohol and drugs. No matter what question I asked, Jake could avoid answering it by shifting the focus to something else. That's what avoidance is all about—getting people to talk about anything except the real problem. Jake was real good at it. He believed that if he could avoid talking about his drinking and drug problem it would just go away. Unfortunately, Jake's dead. He relapsed and got killed in a drunk-driving accident. Here is another story that exposes avoidance:

There was once a carpenter who had an accident with a power saw. He cut the artery in his wrist. He solved the problem by convincing himself that the cut artery would go away if he didn't think or talk about the fact he was bleeding to death.

Challenging Avoidance

Once the avoidance pattern is exposed, you can use a four-step process to challenge the effectiveness of the pattern by: (1) pointing out the problems with using avoidance; (2) using therapeutic Injunctions to challenge avoidance; (3) using therapeutic permission to challenge avoidance; and (4) using inner dialogue to challenge avoidance. Let's look at these methods in more detail.

Pointing Out the Problem with Using Avoidance: You can do this by saying, *"The problem with using avoidance is that it doesn't work. Jake found that out the hard way. He died a horrible death in a drunk-driving accident. I'm sure his last words were, 'If I don't think about how bad this accident is, it will go away!' Unfortunately, most problems don't just go away. If we don't deal with them they just keep getting worse."*

Therapeutic Injunctions: You can give a therapeutic injunction against using avoidance by saying, *"You don't have to avoid looking at this problem. You don't have to keep on pretending that if you don't look at what's going on things will get better. You owe yourself better than that. Trying to avoid the problem will only make things worse."*

Therapeutic Permission: You can give clients permission to stop avoiding and deal directly with the problem by saying, *"It's OK to take an open and honest look at what's going on.*

You can do it. You owe yourself the truth. Then you can decide on the best way to handle the situation. If you try to turn your back on the problem and pretend it's not there, you will end up getting blindsided later on. What have you got to lose? If it doesn't work you can have double your misery back!"

Teaching Self-Management for Avoidance

To teach your clients how to manage avoidance, you need to focus on two areas: managing avoidance in *clinical sessions* and in *real life.*

Managing Avoidance in Clinical Sessions: This involves three techniques: Establishing the Time-Out Signal, Repeating Trigger Questions, and Shifting between Content and Process. Let's look at each of these in more detail.

Establishing the Time-Out Signal: It is important to set up a signal so that clients can stop the session the first moment they notice themselves moving into avoidance. Many therapists use the "time-out signal" that referees use in football games. Ask the client to use the time-out signal any time they sense themselves starting to use avoidance. It is also important for the therapist to get their client's permission to use the time-out signal if they think the client is slipping back into avoidance. Feedback from the therapist is very important. Most clients have such a strong, unconscious habit of using denial they don't recognize when they lapse into it.

Repeating Trigger Questions: You teach clients to manage avoidance in clinical sessions by getting them to agree to repeat the same sequence of questions that just activated the avoidance. Ask them to monitor themselves for the signs they are slipping into their old habit of avoiding and changing the subject.

Shifting between Content and Process: The goal of denial self-management is to be able to change the focus of the session from answering questions about the target problem to examining the here-and-now communication process that is preventing clients from looking at the problem. In other words, shift from working on problem solving to working on changing how clients are thinking and communicating that prevents recognizing and solving the problem.

Managing Avoidance in Real Life: The basic techniques are: (1) conscious self-monitoring; (2) recognition and thought stopping; and (3) refocusing on problem solving. Let's look at each of these in more detail.

Conscious Self-Monitoring: This involves creating a self-monitoring card for the cognitive themes and behavioral consequences of avoiding and asking clients to do an inventory of their thoughts and behaviors four times per day. A typical schedule for self-monitoring is in the morning when they get up, at lunchtime, at dinnertime, and before bed. The self-monitoring sheet should contain no more than three to five critical indicators that they are using the avoidance denial pattern. The most critical indicators of avoidance are (1) refusing to think or talk about the problem when you know it's important to do so, (2) keeping yourself preoccupied with thinking about doing other things, (3) constantly changing the subject and controlling conversation to keep the problem area from coming up, and (4) feeling fearful, anxious, or nervous that the problem will come up in conversation.

Recognition and Thought Stopping: Whenever clients recognize they have started to use avoidance they need to practicing a thought-stopping method. This method involves the following steps: Step 1: Consciously recognizing and affirming the use of the denial pattern by saying, *"I'm starting to use avoidance again. This isn't helpful! This won't work! I owe myself better than this!"* Step 2: Making a conscious decision to either stop this way of thinking or consciously continue by saying, *"OK, what do I want to do? I'm in the habit of avoiding this issue but I know it doesn't do any good and just makes me feel worse. Do I want to stop avoiding and start focusing on problem solving, or do I want to have an episode of intense, irrational avoidance to get this out of my system?"*

If clients choose to have an intense episode of irrational avoidance, they should do so in a deliberate and conscious fashion by writing a list of things they could do to avoid thinking or talking about the problem. Then they can rate each item on the list using a scale going from plus ten (extremely self-enhancing) to minus ten (extremely self-defeating or self-destructive). Then they can discuss their list with their therapist, at self-help group meetings, and with their sponsor to find new and better ways to consciously distract themselves from the problem when they choose to.

Consciously Practicing Avoidance: I also recommend that clients consciously practice avoidance by setting aside a period of time each day in which they set the goal of not thinking or talking about the core problem. By making the avoidance process conscious and deliberate, the underlying patterns of irrationality will be exposed and the secondary benefits of the irrational thinking will disappear. By consciously evaluating the self-enhancing and self-defeating aspects of different cognitive, behavioral, and situational distractions, clients can learn to redirect their avoidance tendencies by distracting themselves in healthier ways that will enhance their recovery. If clients choose to stop avoiding, they move on to step three.

Using an Immediate Relaxation Technique: Use an immediate relaxation technique to physically relax and become mentally focused. Try to still the mind and break the thought cycle by repeating a meditation such as this: *"I am willing to let go of my need to avoid. I am willing to release and relax and allow my thoughts to freely flow in and out of my mind. I am willing to release and let go of distractions. I am willing to allow thoughts and feelings of the problem to enter my awareness. I am willing to begin to focus on what I need to do in the moment to identify and manage this problem. I am relaxing and becoming focused on my needs in the moment."*

Conscious Inner Dialogue: Conduct a conscious inner dialogue between the Avoiding Self and the Responsible Self.

Refocusing on Problem Solving: To consciously refocus on problem solving, clients should review a written statement of the problem, the goal, and the action plan for dealing with it. These items are often contained in the treatment plan. Clients then need to focus on where they are in the problem-solving process by asking three questions: (1) Have I identified and clarified the problem? (2) Have I identified different alternative solutions and projected the logical consequences of each? (3) Have I selected, implemented, and evaluated the outcome of one of the alternatives?

Then clients need to challenge themselves with this question: "Is there anything I need to do right now to deal responsibly with the core problem?" If the answer is "yes," start doing it. If the answer is "no," consciously "turn over" the need to focus on the problem by saying, *"I'm doing everything I need to do to responsibly manage the problem. Problem resolution takes time. The pot is on the stove, and now I need to wait for it to boil. I need to focus on other productive things until it's time to act on the next step."* Then get involved in doing something else productive for your recovery, health, and well-being.

3-2: Absolute Denial

Clients using absolute denial don't admit they have a problem despite convincing evidence. Every time the problem is pointed out, they adamantly refuse having it. At times, they are offended that the therapist even suggests they are the kind of people who would have such a problem. When focused questioning and active listening fail, it's time to use the intervention steps of the Denial Management Interactional Process.

Identifying Absolute Denial

Absolute denial is marked by the irrational assertion that there is no problem when there is clear evidence that a problem exists.

Gut Reactions: Therapists will often shift between two gut reactions: insecurity and anger. They feel *insecure,* because they tend to believe their clients and doubt themselves. This is because clients using absolute denial are very convincing and they often believe what they are saying. As a result they often show no clues commonly associated with lying. So it's easy to believe the client and doubt your own instincts.

Therapists can feel *angry* because clients won't acknowledge the problem. Absolute denial can be so irrational that it's hard to believe that clients can possibly be serious. I once had a client deny there was a relationship between his drinking and getting a ticket for drunk driving. *"You don't understand,"* he told me. *"That cop had it out for me and would have gotten me on something even if I wasn't drinking. Besides, no matter what the breathalyzer says, I wasn't drunk!"*

Nonverbal Indicators: Clients in absolute denial can become *argumentative, pushy, aggressive,* and *defensive.* They have a strong need to be right and a strong need for you to agree with them. The nonverbal behavior associated with absolute denial gives this message: "Why don't you be reasonable and admit that I really don't have a problem?" or "How could you be so stupid (or rude, mean, or crazy) to accuse me of having this problem?"

Behavioral Goals: The goal of absolute denial is to convince yourself and others that you don't have a problem. The client will argue, reason, rationalize, and justify with a single goal in mind—to get you to agree there is nothing really wrong despite the convincing evidence that there is. This leads to a stubborn and inflexible refusal to consider the possibility that the problem exists. Absolute denial is almost always coupled with other denial patterns such as rationalizing ("I don't have a problem because…") or blaming ("I don't have a problem because it is someone else's fault").

Absolute denial can take two forms: "I don't have a problem." Or a more sophisticated version: "Yes, what you're saying is true, but that doesn't mean I have a problem." Let's look at a typical clinical interview:

Therapist: It's my understanding that you were arrested for driving under the influence of alcohol. Is that true?

Client: Who told you that? I was never arrested. It's not true.

Therapist: Well, then, it seems there was a mistake because the court forwarded me this record of the citation, the court appearance, and the court order for you to be evaluated.

Client: Well, I did go to court, but I didn't think I was actually charged with DUI. I thought that by coming here I'd avoid getting charged. I wasn't drinking, and my drinking isn't a problem anyway. I guess my attorney really screwed things up. I'll call him and have him fix everything.

Cognitive Themes and Self-Talk: The cognitive theme of absolute denial is: "I don't have a problem!" People insist there is nothing wrong despite clear evidence that something is wrong. They focus their attention on creating a long list of reasons why the problem can't exist.

One key to interrupting absolute denial is to know that the people who use it usually have an *internal conflict.* One part of them is saying, "I don't have a problem," while another part is saying, "Oh yes I do!" This inner conflict is called *cognitive dissonance.* People using absolute denial also tend to be angry because the therapist is forcing them to think and talk about a painful problem that feels overwhelming. The strategy is to make the therapist part of the problem by getting them to accept "The Big Lie"—the assertion that "I don't have a problem" when there is clear evidence that "I do have a problem."

People using absolute denial also set therapists up by inviting them to fight. The basic unspoken challenge is, "I don't have a problem. How dare you say I do! It's up to you to prove it to me." If the therapist accepts this invitation, clients can easily move back into avoidance by starting an argument and using a technique called "Uproar." Or they can get the therapist to play the game called "Guess what my problem is." Then, when the therapist makes a wrong guess, clients can focus on the "nonproblem" and can talk about something other than the core problem. As a result, when clients fail to make progress because they are not working on the core issue, they can blame the therapist for working on the wrong thing.

Mistaken Beliefs: The primary mistaken belief is this: *"If I can convince myself and others I don't have a problem, it will be solved."* This is a mistaken belief because a real problem exists whether or not clients are convinced it's a problem. If a judge orders me to court and I convince myself that the judge never issued the order, there will still be consequences. If I break a leg and convince myself that nothing is wrong, I will still have problems walking.

Exposing Absolute Denial

You can expose absolute denial in the following way:

Stating the Problem: You can say, *"What I'm hearing you say is that you don't believe you have a problem despite all the evidence that shows you do have a problem. Am I hearing you correctly?"*

Asking for Problem Verification: Ask, *"Do you believe you have this problem?"* Clients using absolute denial will either say they don't have the problem or try to shift to a different denial pattern, usually back to avoidance.

Presenting the Evidence: To stop absolute denial therapists must present evidence that the problem does exist. It is best to avoid a head-on power struggle by using a technique I call the Columbo Method, which is a clinical technique modeled after the television detective named Columbo. Columbo would get suspects to give him more information by playing dumb and trying to get them to explain in detail why they couldn't possibly have committed the crime. Here is how to present the evidence using a Columbo style.

Therapist: What I'm hearing you say is that you don't have a problem with either drinking or drug use. Is that correct?

Client: Yes, that's right.

Therapist: Your answer makes me a little bit confused. I'm wondering if you can help me straighten things out.

Client: Sure.

Therapist: Since you don't have a drinking problem, I'm wondering why you have two previous arrests for driving under the influence of alcohol. Is that a mistake?

Client: No. It's a not a mistake. I did get two DUI's.

Therapist: Do you consider the DUI's a problem?

Client: Well, yes. But it doesn't mean I have a drinking problem.

Therapist: What I'm hearing you say is that getting arrested for DUI doesn't mean that you have a drinking problem. Is that correct?

Client: That's right. A lot of people get arrested for DUI. It doesn't mean they're an alcoholic or an addict.

Therapist: I see. How did your wife react to the two DUI's?

Client: She didn't like it. If I can't drive, I can't get to work. No work, no paycheck. She really got on my case. I ended up sleeping on the couch for a week.

Therapist: Do you consider the arguments with your wife and a week of sleeping on the couch a problem?

Client: Yes, but it's got nothing to do with my drinking. You know how women are!

Therapist: So let me make sure I'm understanding you. You've been arrested twice for DUI, but that doesn't mean you have a drinking problem. Your wife was so upset about your last DUI arrest that you had a bad fight and slept on the couch for a week. But that doesn't mean you have a drinking problem. Is this correct?

The therapist keeps probing for more and more evidence of a problem and presents the growing list of problems to the client, constantly repeating the assertion that "That problem doesn't mean I have a drinking problem!"

Eventually the mistaken belief that underlies absolute denial gets exposed: That mistaken belief is, "If I can convince myself and others I don't have a problem, the problem will be solved."

Educating about Absolute Denial

The next step is to educate clients about absolute denial.

Description: You can briefly describe absolute denial by saying, *"What you are doing seems an awful lot like a denial pattern called absolute denial. Do you know what absolute denial is?"* If clients answer "yes," ask them to explain their understanding of absolute denial and then focus on clarifying and correcting their answer by using active listening. If clients answer "no," go to the next step and give them a mini-education session about absolute denial.

Education: You can say, *"Absolute denial is a way of dealing with a problem by trying to convince yourself and others that you couldn't possibly have the problem. People use absolute denial because, on some level, they believe they might have the problem, but it is easier to deny the problem rather than to find out for sure. The mistaken belief that drives absolute denial is, "I don't care what the facts are, my mind is made up. If I deny the problem strongly enough it will go away."*

Stories and Analogies: The next step is to tell the client an instructive story or analogy about absolute denial. Here's one that often works well: *Turning Your Back to the Train:*

There was once a man standing on a railroad track. He looked down the track, and in the distance he could see an express train coming toward him. He knew he had a problem and needed to do something to solve it.

So he turned around, put his back toward the train, and looked down the empty tracks in the other direction. He breathed a sigh of relief and said to himself, "Problem solved! Now there is no train coming my way."

Here's another story that works well is: *I Don't Care about the Facts, My Mind's Made Up:*

A man who was being tried for murder was undergoing cross examination by the prosecuting attorney. The prosecutor presented him with fact after fact that clearly showed he must have committed the murder. Out of desperation the man turned to his last possible defense. He looked the prosecutor in the eye and said, "I don't care what the facts are. My mind is made up. I am innocent!"

Examples Of Others: You can then ask, *"Have you ever tried to talk with someone about a serious concern and they kept denying the problem despite clear evidence they had the problem?"*

Personal Examples: Then you can ask clients if they have ever used absolute denial by saying, *"Most people use absolute denial when they have a serious problem they don't want to face. Sometimes it's just easier to deny the problem and hope it will go away than it is to face the problem and try to solve it. Have you ever used absolute denial to keep from thinking or talking about a problem that you knew was serious? Tell me about it."*

Challenging Absolute Denial

Pointing Out the Problem with Using Absolute Denial: The first thing to do is to point out that absolute denial doesn't work by saying, *"You know that denying the problem won't make it go away. You may forget about it for a while, but the problem will still be there. When walking through a minefield, it doesn't do any good to close your eyes and try to convince yourself there are no landmines in the ground. You'd be better off walking around the minefield or learning how to find the landmines to avoid accidentally stepping on one."*

Therapeutic Injunctions: You can say, *"You don't have to deny the problem. It's OK to look at what's really going on!"*

Therapeutic Permission: You can say, *"It's OK to take an honest look at what's really happening. If something is wrong, you can deal with it. If nothing is wrong, you can move on with confidence to deal with something else."*

Inner Dialogue: The final step is to facilitate an inner dialogue between the Denying Self (the part of the self that wants to avoid reality) and the Accepting Self (the part of the self that wants to know reality in order to deal with it effectively). This can be done by taking your clients through the following process: Once the problem and its consequences are exposed, focus on the cognitive dissonance that almost always accompanies absolute denial. Whenever one part of the personality defends against the recognition of a problem by saying, "No, not me!" another part of the personality is usually questioning that conclusion by saying, "Wait, maybe there is a problem here!" This cognitive dissonance shows up in an internal argument between the two parts of the self. The goal is to expose the argument and challenge the part of the personality that is denying the problem.

The cognitive dissonance that underlies absolute denial can be exposed by saying something like this: *"Even though I am hearing you say you don't have a problem, it seems to me there might be a part of you that isn't so sure. Is there a part of you that sometimes thinks you might have a problem? Can I talk to that part of you for a moment?"*

Once the inner conflict has been exposed it can be resolved by having an inner dialogue between both parts of the self with the goal of resolving it. One way to set up an inner dialogue is to ask the client: *"Do you ever have inner conversations with yourself about why all of this is happening to you? Do you ever ask yourself why everyone thinks you have a problem when you know you don't? When you ask yourself these questions, how do you usually answer yourself?"*

Remember that absolute denial means inner dissonance. Inner dissonance means an active conflict between two parts of the self. This inner conflict can be resolved by having a conscious inner dialogue with both parts of the self that are in conflict. To resolve this conflict you can help the client identify both parts of the self and consciously engage in an inner dialogue. Here's an example of how it works:

Therapist: Is there a part of you that is capable of denying that a problem exists even when that problem is obvious to other people?

Client: I guess so. Sometimes I can be pretty pig-headed. When I finally see the truth, I'm amazed I couldn't see it before.

Therapist: Will you tell me more about that? (The client then tells of a past experience when they denied an obvious problem.)

Therapist: What I'm hearing you say is that part of you believes that the problem will go away if you can convince yourself you don't have it. Is that correct?

Client: Yea, I guess so.

Therapist: Let's give it a name. Let's call it your *Denying Self.* Is there another part of you that knows serious problems won't go away just because you don't want to believe they are there?

Client: Yea, sometimes I can see that if I don't take things more seriously I'm going to get into deep trouble.

Therapist: Let's name that part of yourself. Let's call the part of you that is willing to recognize the problem your *Accepting Self.* Can you tell me about some experiences you have had when your *Accepting Self* was in charge? (The client explains several experiences that occurred when his *Accepting Self* was in charge and they were able to accurately assess and openly deal with problems.) Now the stage is set to facilitate an inner dialogue between the Denying Self and the Accepting Self.

Using Rating the Evidence to Challenge Absolute Denial:
Another useful technique for challenging absolute denial is to help clients make a list of all reasons why they can't have the problem. Then ask them to rate how strongly they believe each reason to be on scale of zero to ten. A zero means they don't believe it at all. A ten means they believe it 100 percent.

This technique does several things. First, it forces the client to consciously identify all of the arguments they use in their mind to convince themselves they don't have a problem. Then it helps them to detach from each argument by rating how strongly they believe each reason. This sets the stage for getting into an inner dialogue between the part of the self that believes each reason and the part of the self that doubts each reason.

Using Changing the Point of View to Challenge Absolute Denial: Another technique to expose absolute denial is to ask clients to explain why other people think they might have a problem. You can say something like this, *"I understand you don't think you have a problem, but obviously the judge [or boss or wife] does. Why do you think the judge believes you have a drinking problem?"*

Then using active listening the therapist and client develop a list of all the reasons why other people are making the mistake of thinking they have the target problem. The therapist then explores what changes the client could make to remove the appearance they have a problem.

This method usually results in the client building a list of reasons why others think they have a problem that convinces them they do have a problem. Many clients are often unwilling or unable to make any changes to eliminate "the appearance" that they have a problem. This can be used as convincing evidence that a problem really does exist.

Teaching Self-Management for Absolute Denial

Here's how we can teach clients how to managing absolute denial:

Managing Absolute Denial in Clinical Sessions: First, use a time-out signal so that both client and therapist can stop the session the moment they first notice the client moving into absolute denial. Second, repeat the trigger questions by asking clients to repeat the same sequence of questions that just activated the absolute denial. Ask them to monitor themselves for the signs they are slipping into their old habit of denying the problem. Then shift the focus from content to process by examining the here-and-now communication process that is preventing the client from looking at the problem.

A good method for teaching clients to manage absolute denial is to teach them how to keep an open mind to the possibility they might have a problem. Many clients find if they start talking about their view of a problem with the words "I might be wrong, but this is how I see things." It gives them room to see things from a different point of view.

Another technique is to use Point-of-View Training by asking clients to try and figure out how other people are seeing things from their point of view. By asking clients to change their point of view, their perception of the problem usually begins to change and they start to see that maybe they do have a problem.

Managing Absolute Denial in Real Life: First, use conscious self-monitoring by creating a self-monitoring card for the cognitive themes and behavioral consequences of blaming. Then ask clients to do an inventory four times per day. The critical indicators of absolute denial are (1) refusing to think or talk about the problem when you know that it's important to do so, (2) keeping yourself preoccupied with thinking about doing other things, (3) constantly changing the subject and controlling conversation to keep the problem area from coming up, and (4) feeling fearful, anxious, or nervous that the problem will come up in conversation.

Recognition and Thought Stopping: Whenever the client recognizes they have started to use absolute denial they need to practice a thought-stopping method. This method involves the following steps: Step 1: Consciously recognizing and affirming the use of the denial pattern (saying something like, *"I'm starting to use absolute denial again. This isn't helpful! This won't work! I owe myself better than this."* Step 2: Making a conscious decision to stop this way of thinking or consciously continue by saying something like, *"OK, what do I want to do? I'm in the habit of denying this issue, but I know it doesn't do any good and just makes me feel worse. Do I want to stop denying and start focusing on problem solving, or do I want to have an episode of intense irrational denial to get this out of my system?"*

If they choose to have an intense episode they should do so in a deliberate and conscious fashion by: (1) writing a list of distracting or preoccupying behaviors, activities, and thoughts; (2) evaluating each distracting or preoccupying thought, behavior, and activity on a plus-ten minus-ten scale for its self-enhancing and self-destructive potential (a score of plus ten means it is extremely self-enhancing or beneficial; a score of minus 10 means it is extremely self-defeating or self-destructive); (3) discussing their list with their therapist, at self-help group meetings, and with their sponsor to find new and better ways to consciously distract themselves from the problem; and (4) setting the conscious goal to not allow any thought of the core problem to come into or to stay in their mind for more than a brief moment.

By making the denial process conscious and deliberate, the underlying patterns of irrationality will be exposed and the secondary benefits of the irrational thinking will disappear. By consciously evaluating the self-enhancing and self-defeating aspects of different cognitive, behavioral, and situational distractions, clients can learn to redirect their denial tendencies by distracting themselves in healthy ways that will enhance their recovery.

Refocusing on Problem Solving: To consciously refocus on the problem, clients should review a written statement of the problem, the goal, and the action plan for dealing with it. These items are often contained on the treatment plan. Clients then need to focus on where they are in the problem-solving process by asking three questions: (1) Have I identified and clarified the problem? (2) Have I identified different alternative solutions and projected the logical consequences of each? (3) Have I selected, implemented, and evaluated the outcome of one of the alternatives?

Then clients can challenge themselves with this question: "Is there anything I need to do right now to deal responsibly with the core problem?" If the answer is "yes," start doing it. If the answer is "no," consciously "turn over" the need to focus on the problem and focus on other productive things until it is time to act on the next step.

3-3: Minimizing

Clients who minimize admit they have a problem but keep insisting that the problem isn't that bad.

Identifying Minimizing

To identify minimizing you can look at the following:

Gut Reactions: Therapists often experience: (1) The need to force the client to see how bad the problem really is, or (2) the need to agree that the problem isn't very bad in order to avoid confronting the client. It is easy for therapists to become annoyed with clients who ignore the evidence and irrationally argue that the problem isn't serious when it really is. These clients want their therapists to confront them and try to convince them that the problem really is bad by saying something like this, *"What's the matter with you? Are you stupid? Can't you see what's really going on? Open your eyes and smell the coffee! You're in deep trouble! Why can't you see that?"* The therapists who give in to this urge almost always become part of their clients problems instead of guiding them to a solution.

Ultimately, clients who are using minimizing want some kind of official sanction from their therapists that their problems really aren't bad and that they don't need to work at recovery. Minimizing clients can be so convincing that therapists can lose touch with the evidence and inadvertently agree that the problem isn't that bad. Therapists can also get tired of arguing with nonreceptive clients and tell them what they want to hear just to end the argument. They can then select an irrelevant issue that the client is motivated to work on and convince themselves that they are really helping the clients.

Nonverbal Indicators: Clients who are minimizing often take on a flippant or condescending attitude. Therapists get the message that they are somehow insulting their clients by suggesting that they have a serious problem. The client's nonverbal message, if put into words, would go something like this: *"How could you possibly think I have a serious problem? Yes, there is a problem, but it's not as bad as you think. If you think this is a serious problem, there must be something wrong with you."* This nonverbal challenge puts therapists on the defensive and invites them to prove to the clients just how bad the problem is. One of the worst things therapists can do, of course, is to say yes to that invitation.

Behavioral Goals: The behavioral goal of minimizing is to convince other people that the problem is minor, trivial, or insignificant. Clients who minimize want to believe their problems aren't that serious and that they don't require treatment or a recovery program. On some level minimizing clients believe that if other people will tell them things aren't that bad the problem will magically go away.

Cognitive Themes and Self-Talk: The cognitive theme of minimizing is, "Yes, I have a problem, but it isn't that bad!" Clients who are minimizing tend to say the problem is very minor and other people are just blowing it out of proportion and making a big deal out of it for no reason.

Mistaken Beliefs: The mistaken belief that drives minimizing is this: "If I can convince myself and others the problem isn't that bad, the problem will go away and I won't have to deal with it."

Exposing Minimizing

You can expose minimizing by saying, *"What I'm hearing you say is that you do have a problem, but it isn't that bad. Other people think the problem is worse than it is. Is that correct?"*

Educating about Minimizing

You can educate about minimizing by using the following methods:

Description: Describe minimizing by saying, *"What you're doing is called minimizing. You're trying to convince yourself the problem isn't very bad so you don't have to solve it."*

Education: Educate about minimizing by saying, *"Minimizing is a way of dealing with a painful or difficult problem by convincing yourself the problem isn't very bad and that everyone else mistakenly believes the problem is worse than it really is. People minimize because they believe on some level that if they can convince themselves and others that the problem isn't very bad, the problem will go away."*

Examples of Others: Ask clients for examples of other people who use minimizing by asking, *"Have you ever tried to* talk with someone who has a serious problem and they kept telling you the problem wasn't that bad even though you could clearly see it was? Will you tell me about that experience?"

Personal Examples: Ask the client for personal examples of minimizing by saying, *"From time to time most of us minimize the seriousness of our problems. Sometimes it's just easier to deal with the problem by convincing ourselves it just isn't as bad as everyone thinks it is. On some level we believe that if we can convince ourselves the problem isn't very bad, then the problem will go away and we won't have to deal with it. Have you ever used minimizing to keep from thinking or talking about a problem you knew was serious? Tell me about it?*

Stories and Analogies about Minimizing: There are a number of stories and analogies that can quickly expose the fundamental problems with minimizing:

A Prostitute No Matter the Price:

There was a man who asked a beautiful woman if she would have sex with him for a million dollars. He opened up a briefcase and showed her the stacks of hundred-dollar bills. The woman thought about it for a moment and then said, "Yes, I'll have sex with you for a million dollars." Then the man asked, "Will you have sex with me for ten dollars?" The woman got angry and felt offended. "Of course not," she replied! "What do you think I am?" He said, "I thought we had already established that and we were just haggling about the price." When people start minimizing they have accepted that they have a problem. You are just haggling about how bad the problem is.

A Little Bit Pregnant:

One young woman went to her doctor complaining of feeling sick in the morning. After doing several tests the doctor told her she was in the second month of pregnancy. The woman looked at the doctor and said, "Thank God it isn't that bad. I'm just a little bit pregnant so there's nothing to worry about."

It Is but a Flesh Wound:

A good knight was guarding a bridge when two evil

knights approached and wanted to pass. The good knight refused passage and the evil knights attacked him. The evil knights cut off the good knight's left arm and asked him to surrender. The good knight refused by saying, "It is but a flesh wound!" and kept right on fighting. Then the evil knights cut off his left leg and once again asked him to surrender. The good knight again refused to surrender saying, "It is but another flesh wound." Hobbling on his one good leg and holding his sword in his one remaining arm the good knight kept right on fighting. Then the evil knights cut off his right leg and asked him to surrender for the third time, and again the good knight refused saying, "It is but another flesh wound." Balancing precariously on his two bleeding stumps that were once his legs, the good knight brandished his sword with his one remaining arm and kept fighting. Finally the evil knights cut off his only remaining arm and began to ride past the now helpless, good knight to cross the bridge. As they road by the good knight yelled. "It takes more than four minor flesh wounds to defeat me. Don't run away you cowards. Come back and fight me like men!"

Challenging Minimizing

Pointing out the Problem with Using Minimizing: You can show that minimizing doesn't work by saying, *"You know that minimizing your problems won't make them go away. You may convince yourself your problems are not bad enough to worry about, but the problems will still be there and they will still be as bad as they really are. If you cut an artery and convince yourself it's a small scratch, you will bleed to death. If you have a heart attack and convince yourself it's just indigestion, you may well die. Minimizing just isn't a very good problem-solving strategy and it can be fatal."*

Therapeutic Injunctions: You can give a therapeutic injunction against using minimizing by saying, *"You don't have to minimize your problems. You owe yourself better than that. It's OK to look at what's really going on and make an accurate assessment of how bad things really are!"*

Therapeutic Permission: You can give clients permission to challenge minimizing by saying, *"It's OK to stop minimizing and take an honest look at how bad your problems really are. Then you can decide what to do about it."*

Inner Dialogue: The final step to facilitate an inner dialogue between the Minimizing Self (the part of the self that wants to avoid reality) and the Accurate Self (the part of the self that wants to know what reality is in order to effectively deal with it). It is also helpful to realize that one of the things that drives people to minimize is a Catastrophizing Self that makes problems seem worse than they really are. When a client is asked to identify the Accurate Self, they often connect with their "inner Catastrophizer" and begin trying to convince you the problems are so bad they can't be handled. This sets the stage to transition into the denial pattern of strategic hopelessness.

This can be done by taking your clients through the following process: Clients using minimizing will readily acknowledge there is a problem. They will argue that the problem is not very serious when it really is. Expose the problem and ask clients to describe how serious they think the problem is. This usually surfaces an inner dissonance between the Minimizing Self and the Accurate Self. Whenever one part of the personality defends against a problem by saying, "It's not that bad!" another part of the personality is usually questioning that conclusion by saying *"Wait, maybe it's worse than you think! Maybe this problem is so bad we should take it seriously."* This cognitive dissonance shows up in an internal argument between the two parts of the self. The goal is to expose the argument and challenge the part of the personality that is denying the problem.

The cognitive dissonance that underlies minimizing can be exposed by saying something like this: *"Even though I am hearing you say the problem isn't that bad, it seems to me there might be a part of you that isn't so sure. Is there a part of you that sometimes thinks the problem may be worse than you think it is? Can I talk to that part of you for a moment?"*

Once the inner conflict has been exposed, it can be resolved by having *an inner dialogue* between both parts of the self with the goal of resolving it. One way to set up an inner dialogue is to ask the client, *"Do you ever have inner conversations with yourself about how bad this problem really is? Do you ever ask yourself why you think the problem isn't very bad and almost everyone else thinks you have a very serious problem that you should deal with immediately? When you ask yourself these questions, how do you usually answer yourself?"*

Remember that the minimizing denial pattern usually means there is inner dissonance. Inner dissonance means an active conflict between two parts of the self. This inner conflict can be resolved by having a conscious inner dialogue with both parts of the self that are in conflict. To resolve this conflict you can help the client identify both parts of the self and consciously engage in an inner dialogue. Here's an example of how it works with the minimizing denial pattern.

Therapist: Is there a part of you that is capable of convincing yourself a serious problem really isn't as bad as everyone thinks?

Client: I guess so. People are trying to tell me what's wrong and what to do about it. I'm in the habit of just blowing them off. So I guess I can easily convince myself to ignore a problem that I should be dealing with. But that's not what's going on here. I'm sure of it. This problem really isn't as bad as everyone is trying to make it.

Therapist: Will you tell me more about that?

Client: (The client then explains why he or she thinks the problem isn't that serious. The therapist probes to get the reasons why other people think it is serious.)

Therapist: So what I'm hearing you say is that there is a part of you that believes the problem isn't serious even though other people are telling you it is. Is that correct?

Client: Yes. I guess so.

Therapist: Everyone has different parts of their personality. Some of those parts invite us to minimize our problems and see them as less severe than they really are. Other parts of our personality will invite us to catastrophize our problems by seeing them as much worse than they really are. There is also a part of our personality that is capable of accurately assessing, in an objective fashion, how bad our problems are and how important it is to deal with them.

We often don't recognize these parts of our personality because we've never taken the time to think about what goes on inside of us. We've never taken the effort to notice the different parts of our personality or to name them. Without naming them, we can't directly deal with them. And if we can't deal with them they can end up controlling us.

The first step to getting free is to name the part of you that is in charge. It seems to me that you put the minimizing part of your personality in charge a lot of the time. This minimizing part of your personality tries to convince you that *"This problem isn't as bad as it really is!"* Do you agree that this minimizing part of your personality is in charge of your thinking much of the time?

Client: Yea, I guess so.

Therapist: Let's give it a name. Let's call it your Minimizing Self.

Client: OK.

Therapist: Is there another part of you that is capable of accurately assessing how bad a problem is?

Client: Yea, sometimes I can see that a problem is more serious than I first thought it was.

Therapist: Let's name that part of yourself your Accurate Self. Can you tell me about some experiences you have had when your Accurate Self was in charge?

Client: (The client explains several experiences that occurred when the Accurate Self was in charge and they were able to accurately assess and openly deal with problems.)

Now the stage is set to facilitate an inner dialogue between the Minimizing Self and the Accurate Self.

Challenging Minimizing by Rating the Seriousness of the Problem: An effective approach to minimizing is to ask the person, *"How bad do you think the problem is on a ten-point scale, with 1 being not very bad at all and 10 being as bad as it could possibly get?"* When they rate the problem ask them to describe why they rated it that way. Then ask them what a level 1 (a mild version of the problem), a level 5 (a moderate version of the problem), and a level 10 (a very serious or catastrophic version of the problem) would look like.

This will give you detailed information to help them more realistically assess how serious the problem is.

Clients who are minimizing often need to hear how others would rate the seriousness of the problem and why. The ten-point rating scale allows the therapist to move easily into self-disclosure by saying something like this: *"I understand you consider that a problem a three. If I had your problem, however, I think I'd probably rate it as an eight or a nine. Would you like to know why?"* In a group therapy session the therapist can ask the group for feedback by saying something like this: *"John has rated the seriousness of this problem as a three. If you had this problem, how would you rate it and why?"* This can set the stage for group discussion and feedback.

Teaching Self-Management for Minimizing

Teaching self-management for minimizing is essentially the same as with the other denial patterns with one exception: Many people who minimize have been raised in dysfunctional families where severe problems and seriously dysfunctional or self-defeating behaviors were accepted as normal. As a result it is important to teach clients the **Principles of Healthy Behavior** so they can have an objective standard against which to compare their behavior

I recommend teaching clients a five-point standard for healthy behavior: (1) *Healthy behavior promotes life:* Healthy behavior values life and will do what is necessary to protect life, both our own and that of other people; any behavior that puts one at an unusually high risk of dying is probably unhealthy or self-defeating. (2) *Healthy behavior promotes health:* Healthy behavior values physical and psychological health and promotes behaviors and lifestyles that make a person healthier, prevent disease, and recognize and treat disease or mental disorders early; any behavior that increases the risk of physical or psychological illness is probably unhealthy. (3) *Healthy behavior promotes full vitality:* Healthy behavior values full vitality (one of the goals of being healthy is to feel good and to have vibrant good health); any behavior that depletes personal energy, causes chronic fatigue and depression, or creates long depletion of energy as a consequences of a brief period of feeling good is probably unhealthy. (4) *Healthy behavior promotes effective functioning:* Healthy behavior values the ability to be fully functional, to learn and use skills, and demonstrate responsible follow-through on commitments; any behavior that devalues the importance of learning and using skills to function effectively in life is probably unhealthy. (5) *Healthy behavior values effective interpersonal relationships:* Human beings are social animals and some of the most rewarding of all human experiences occur in close relationship with others. Healthy behavior promotes the accurate assessment of other people, building relationships with safe individuals capable of sharing friendship and intimacy, and protecting self from irresponsible people by setting and enforcing appropriate boundaries; any behavior that promotes dysfunctional relationships, the sacrifice of self to others, the sacrifice of others to self, or the total withdrawal from other people is probably unhealthy.

Once these principles are understood, five simple inventory questions can be used to determine on a ten-point scale how unhealthy or destructive a problem or behavior is: (1) To what degree does this problem or behavior increase *my risk of dying?* (2) To what degree does this problem or behavior increase *my risk of becoming ill or injured?* (3) To what degree does this problem or behavior increase *my risk of losing my vitality and feeling drained of energy?* (4) To what degree does this problem or behavior increase *my risk of being sick?* (5) To what degree does this problem or behavior increase *my risk of damaging or destroying my relationships with people I care about or need?*

The critical indicators that can be used in the self-monitoring of minimizing are: (1) The tendency to minimize or downplay the seriousness of the problem, (2) the tendency to dismiss as unimportant any information that shows the problem to be worse than you think it is, and (3) getting angry with people who try to tell you the problem is serious.

3-4: Rationalizing

Clients who rationalize believe that if they can find good

enough reasons for having their problems, the problems will go away.

Identifying Rationalizing

When identifying rationalizing it is helpful to look for these things:

Gut Reactions: You will tend to have the following gut reactions when dealing with clients who are rationalizing: (1) A strong intellectual curiosity with what clients are saying; (2) a tendency to focus on what the client is saying and block out the client's feelings and nonverbal behavior; (3) a strong desire to debate; and (4) a tendency to disconnect from their own feelings and get lost in their head.

Nonverbal Indicators: Clients will typically show three nonverbal indicators that they may be rationalizing: (1) An intellectual and detached attitude; (2) strong focus on arguing and convincing; and (3) resistance to exploring emotional reactions.

Behavioral Goals: The behavioral goal of rationalizing is to avoid adverse consequences by proving there are good reasons for having the problem.

Cognitive Themes and Self-Talk: The basic theme of rationalizing is: "Yes, I have a serious problem, but I also have a good reason for having the problem and therefore the problem doesn't matter." The common self-talk revolves around proving there are good reasons for the problem and that those reasons should make the problem and any adverse consequences disappear.

Mistaken Beliefs: When rationalizing, people tend to believe that if there are good reasons for having the problem, the problem doesn't count and there should be no consequences. Rationalizing can also set the stage to move back into avoidance by shifting the focus from the problem to the "good reasons" for having the problem. The therapist and the client can then spend time arguing about whether the reasons for the problem are "good enough." In that way, the client doesn't have to think about or talk about the problem itself. They can avoid clarifying the problem and developing problem-solving strategies.

Exposing Rationalizing

You can expose rationalizing by saying, *"What I'm hearing you say is that you do have a problem, but because you have good reasons for having it, there should be no consequences?"*

Educating about Rationalizing

The next step is to educate about rationalizing denial:

Description: You can say: *"What you're doing is called rationalizing. It appears you are more interested in making excuses for and creating good reasons for having your problems than you are in solving them. You seem to believe that having good excuses and reasons for your problems will solve them and prevent you from experiencing any adverse consequences."*

Education: You can say, *"Rationalizing is a way of dealing with a painful or difficult problem by justifying the problem and creating good reasons for having it. Rationalizing is driven by the mistaken belief that having a good reason for a problem will either solve the problem or protect your from the adverse consequences of the problem."*

Examples of Others: You can ask for examples of other people who rationalize by saying, *"Have you ever tried to talk with someone who has a serious problem and they kept trying to give you excuses and good reasons for having the problem and by doing so they refused to focus on what they could do to solve the problem? Will you tell me about that experience?"*

Personal Examples: Then you can ask about past experiences involving rationalizing that have already been resolved. You can say, *"Most of us use rationalizing when we have a serious problem that we don't want to deal with at the moment. Sometimes it's just easier to find good reasons for having a problem than it is to solve the problem. It's also easier to make excuses for a problem and use wishful thinking to avoid the consequences than it is to actually solve the problem. On some level we want to believe that if we have good reasons and excuses for the problems, our problems will either be solved or we will not have to experience any adverse consequences as a result of the problem. Have you ever used rationalizing to deal with a serious problem? Tell me about it."*

Stories and Analogies: Here is a story that can quickly expose the fundamental problems with rationalizing: *Shooting Off Your Toes:*

There was a man who was in the habit of getting up each morning, taking out a pistol, and shooting off one of his toes. He always had a good reason for shooting off the toe, but despite all of his good reasons, he still didn't walk very well.

Challenging Rationalizing

Pointing Out the Problem with Using Rationalizing: First we need to point out that it doesn't work by saying, *"You know that rationalizing your problems won't make them go away. You may convince yourself your problems are not bad enough to worry about, but the problems will still be there and they will still be as bad as they really are. If you cut an artery and convince yourself it's a small scratch you will bleed to death. If you have a heart attack and convince yourself it's just indigestion you may well die. Rationalizing just isn't a very good problem-solving strategy, and it can be fatal."*

Therapeutic Injunctions: We can give a therapeutic injunction against using rationalizing by saying, *"You don't have to invest time and energy in making excuses for and finding good reasons why you have your problems. The best reasons in the world won't solve the problems. You owe yourself better than that."*

Therapeutic Permission: You can say, *"It's OK to stop thinking about why you have your problems and to start figuring out how to solve them! You can stop trying to find good reasons for having the problem and start investing your time and energy into figuring out how you can solve the problems."*

Inner Dialogue: You can facilitate an inner dialogue between the Rationalizing Self (the part of the self that wants to focus on finding good reasons and excuses for having the problem) and the Problem-Solving Self (the part of the self that wants to solve the problem and effectively deal with the consequences). Clients using rationalizing will acknowledge that there are problems, but they will be intent in finding reasons and excuses for having them. They will also be resistant to finding and implementing solutions. They will argue that having good reasons and excuses for the problem will somehow solve it or eliminate the negative consequences.

The cognitive dissonance that underlies rationalizing can be exposed by saying something like this: *"Even though I am hearing you say you have good reasons for having the problem, it seems to me there is a part of you that is more concerned with solving the problem than with figuring out why you have it. Is there a part of you that sometimes thinks you are investing too much time and energy in finding reasons for having the problem and not enough time and energy into trying to solve the problem? Can I talk to that part of you for a moment?"*

Once the inner conflict has been exposed it can be resolved by having an inner dialogue between both parts of the self with the goal of resolving it. One way to set up an inner dialogue is to ask the client, *"Do you ever have inner conversations with yourself about why you have this problem and how you can solve it? Do you ever get preoccupied with finding good reasons for the problem or making good excuses when others point out the problem to you? Is there a part of you that wants to solve the problem rather than just find reasons and excuses for having it?"* Here's an example of how it works with the rationalizing denial pattern.

Therapist: Is there a part of you that is focused on finding good reasons for having the problem and giving good excuses when others try to talk about the problem with you?

Client: I guess so. People just don't understand how tough this has been for me. They can't seem to see that I didn't deliberately create this problem; there are factors beyond my control that created it. If they could just see the good reason for the problem they'd leave me alone.

Therapist: So what I'm hearing you say is that there is a part of you that spends a lot of time and energy creating reasons and excuses for having the problem. This part of you seems to believe that if you find good enough reasons for the problem all of its negative consequences will go away. Is that correct?

Client: Yes, I guess so. I do spend a lot of time trying to figure out how this could have happened to me.

Therapist: Let's give that excuse-making part of you a name. Let's call it your Rationalizing Self. Is there another part of you that is more interested in solving the problem than in making good excuses for having it?

Client: Of course I want to solve the problem. I keep asking why I can't. But every time I try to solve the problem I end up back in the process of finding reasons or making excuses for it.

Therapist: Let's call the part of you that wants to solve the problem your Problem-Solving Self. Do you ever have inner conversations between your Rationalizing Self (that focuses on finding reasons and excuses) and your Problem-Solving Self (that focuses on finding solutions) so you can see that your Rationalizing Self is very strong?

Client: Yes, I do.

Therapist: Can you describe a typical conversation to me? When you start thinking about the problem, which part of you kicks in first?

Client: My Rationalizing Self starts asking why I have the problem and what's wrong with me that I can't solve it.

Therapist: How does your Problem-Solving Self answer?

Now the stage is set to facilitate an inner dialogue between the Minimizing Self and the Accurate Self.

Challenging Rationalizing by Integrating Thinking, Feeling, and Acting: Another effective way to interrupt denial is to integrate thinking, feeling, and acting. We will explain this system in more detail in the Denial Management Section. The technique can be so effective in stopping rationalizing that I want to briefly explain it here.

First, ask your rationalizing clients to write down the problem and a list of all the reasons and excuses they can think of for having it. Arrange the list of reasons in order of importance with the most important reasons at the top. Then ask the following questions about each of the reasons and process the answers with active listening. The questions are: (1) When you are thinking about the reason for having the problem, what do you tend to feel? (2) When you are feeling that way, what do you have an urge to do? (3) When you have urges like that, what do you usually end up doing? (4) When you do things like that what do other people think of you and how do they usually react to you? (5) When people see you in that way and react to you in that way, how do you usually feel about it? This series of questions normally changes the client's perspective and helps them see the thinking, feeling, behavioral, and social dynamics of the problem.

Teaching Self-Management for Rationalizing

The basic self-management skills for rationalizing involve the ability to recognize when the focus shifts from solving the problem to creating reasons and excuses for having the problem.

Managing Rationalizing in Clinical Sessions: First, set up the time-out signal so that clients can stop the session the first moment they notice themselves using rationalizing. Then repeat the trigger questions that activated the rationalizing and ask clients to monitor themselves for rationalizing.

Then shift the focus from content to process by changing the focus of the session from answering questions about the target problem to examining the here-and-now communication process that is preventing clients from looking at the problem.

Managing Rationalizing in Real Life: The basic steps for teaching clients how to manage rationalizing in real life are as follows:

Conscious Self-Monitoring: Create a self-monitoring card for the cognitive themes and behaviors associated with rationalizing. These are: (1) The tendency to invest time and energy in creating elaborate excuses or reasons for having the problem; (2) the tendency to create reasons why the problem is not your fault; (3) the tendency to search out people to blame for causing you to have the problem; and (4) the tendency to start blaming others whenever other people want to talk about what can be done to solve the problem.

Then ask clients to do an inventory of their thoughts and behaviors four times per day (once in the morning when they get up, once at lunchtime, once at dinnertime and once before bed).

Recognition and Thought Stopping: Whenever clients recognize that they have started to use rationalizing, they need to practice a thought-stopping method. This method involves the following steps: (1) Consciously recognizing and affirming the use of the denial pattern (saying something like, *"I'm starting to use rationalizing again. This isn't helpful! This won't work! I owe myself better than this.*); (2) making a conscious decision to stop this way of thinking or consciously continue, (saying something like, *"OK, what do I want to do? I'm in the habit of rationalizing this issue but I know it doesn't do any good and just makes me feel worse. Do I want to stop rationalizing and start focusing on problem solving, or do I want to have an episode of intense rationalizing to get this out of my system?"*); (3) if they choose to have an intense episode of rationalizing, they should do so in a deliberate and conscious fashion by taking a sheet of paper and dividing it into two columns (In the first column they should write a list of all the reasons and excuses they can think of for having the problem. In the second column they should write a list of how knowing about that reason or excuse will help them solve the problem and have a better life. When that is done they should discuss the list with their therapist, at self-help group meetings, and with their sponsor to find new and better ways to prove the problem really isn't as bad as everyone thinks it is.); and (4) setting the conscious goal to avoid productive problem solving and focus exclusively on making excuses and finding reasons for having the problem. By making the rationalizing process conscious and deliberate the underlying patterns of irrationality will be exposed and the secondary benefits of the irrational thinking will disappear.

If they choose to stop rationalizing, move on to the next step.

Immediate Relaxation Techniques: Use an immediate relaxation technique to physically relax and become mentally focused. Try to still the mind and break the thought cycle by repeating a meditation such as this: *"I am willing to let go of my need to rationalize. I am willing to relax and allow my thoughts to freely flow in and out of my mind. I am willing to let go of all reasons and excuses for having this problem. I am willing to allow thoughts and feelings about how to solve the* problem to enter my awareness. I am willing to begin to focus on objectively evaluating how serious the problem is and what I need to do in the moment to identify and manage this problem. I am relaxing and becoming focused on my needs in the moment."

Conscious Inner Dialogue: Conduct a conscious inner dialogue between the Minimizing Self and the Accurate Self.

Refocus on Problem Solving: To consciously refocus on the problem, clients should review a written statement of the problem, the goal, and the action plan for dealing with it. (These items are often contained in the treatment plan.) Clients then need to focus on where they are in the problem-solving process by asking the following questions: (1) Have I identified and clarified the problem? (2) Have I identified different alternative solutions and projected the logical consequences of each? (3) Have I selected, implemented, and evaluated the outcome of one of the alternatives (4) Is there anything I need to do right now to deal responsibly with the core problem? If the answer is "yes," start doing it. If the answer is "no," consciously "turn over" the need to focus on the problem by saying, *"I'm doing everything I need to do to manage the problem responsibly."* Then get busy doing something else.

3-5: Blaming

Clients who use blaming acknowledge that there is a problem, but they avoid personal responsibility for solving the problem by finding other people to blame. They will argue that having someone to blame for the problem will somehow solve it or eliminate the negative consequences. They believe the person responsible should be able to magically remove all adverse consequences.

Identifying Blaming

When identifying blaming it is helpful to look for the following:

Gut Reactions: There are three gut-level reactions that can be indicators that clients are shifting from genuine communication into blaming. These are: (1) An urge to defend, rescue, or protect someone being blamed or attacked by the clients: clients will unfairly place the blame for their problems on someone else and by doing so will invite you to defend, rescue, or protect the people being blamed; (2) an urge to attack or confront the clients to make them accept personal responsibility: clients will adamantly refuse to accept personal responsibility and by doing so will invite you to attack or confront them to make them accept personal responsibility; and (3) fear of being attacked or blamed: clients will express such anger and hostility toward others that a natural anxiety or fear will develop in therapists that they will be the next one to be attacked or blamed.

Nonverbal Indicators: There are three nonverbal indicators of blaming: (1) Anger directed at the therapist or someone else; (2) glaring self-righteousness marked by blaming others; and (3) refusing to even consider the possibility that they might have had a role in creating the core problem.

Behavioral Goals: The behavioral goal of blaming is to avoid adverse consequences by proving that someone else is responsible for the problem.

Cognitive Themes and Self-Talk: The cognitive theme of blaming is "Yes, there is a problem, but it's not my fault!" Blaming can also set the stage to move back into avoidance by shifting the focus from the problem itself to the search for who is responsible for causing the problems. The therapist and the client can then spend time arguing about who's at fault instead of clarifying the problem and developing problem-solving strategies.

Mistaken Beliefs: Blaming is driven by this mistaken belief: "If I can prove that someone else is responsible for my problem, I won't have to deal with it." This mistaken belief will create a compulsion within clients to (1) to focus on their own innocence ("It's not my fault!"); (2) avoid or abdicate personal responsibility ("You have no right to expect me to deal with this problem!"); (3) shift responsibility to others ("Since it's their fault, force them to fix it!"); and (4) expect that any adverse consequences of the problem will magically disappear ("It's not fair! Since it's not my fault, nothing should happen to me!). As a result they will feel absolved from any obligation to do anything differently in order to deal with the problem ("Why should I have to do anything since it's not my problem?").

Exposing Blaming

You can expose blaming by doing the following:

Stating the Problem: You can say, *"What I'm hearing you say is that you believe you do have a problem but it's not your fault. Is that correct?"*

Verifying the Problem: Ask: *"Do you believe you are blaming others for the problem and refusing to take personal responsibility for having it?"*

Presenting the Evidence: To stop blaming you need to keep track of all the people who are being blamed for the problem and keep adding to the list. Here's an example:

Client: I don't have a drinking problem! If that cop didn't stop me I wouldn't be here right now.

Therapist: So what I'm hearing you say is that your arrest for drunk driving isn't your fault. It is the fault of the police officer who arrested you. Is that correct?

Client: Yea, I was driving fine. That cop should have left me alone.

Therapist: Is there anyone else who is responsible for your problem?

Client: Yea—the judge who sided with the cop. If the judge would have believed me I wouldn't be here. It's the judge's fault.

Therapist: So what I'm hearing you say is that your arrest for drunk driving is in *no way* your fault. It's the fault of the police officer who arrested you and the judge who sided with the arresting officer. Is that correct?

Client: Yea, you're hearing me now.

Therapist: Is there anyone else who is responsible for your problem? (The therapist keeps asking this question and adding to the list of people who are to blame and the reasons why they are to blame. This process will begin to expose the mistaken belief that drives blaming: "If I can prove that my problem is someone else's fault, the problem will go away!" When the client can't think of anyone else to blame, the therapist can ask, *"What role did you have in causing this problem?"* The therapist then explores what would have happened if the client had not been drinking before driving.)

Educating about Blaming

The next step is to educate about blaming.

Description: Name and describe blaming by saying, *"What you're doing is called blaming. When people start blaming they refuse to accept any responsibility for their problems and are more interested in placing the blame on someone else than they are in trying to solve the problem. People who use blaming to deal with problems believe that if they can find someone to blame, their problems will be solved."*

Education: Explain what blaming is by saying, *"Blaming is a way of dealing with problems by refusing to accept personal responsibility and investing time and energy in blaming other people for causing the problem. Blaming is driven by the mistaken belief that if someone else is responsible for the problem, it will go away."*

Examples of Others: Ask the client for examples of other people who used blaming to cope with a problem by saying, *"Have you ever tried to talk with someone who had a serious problem who was more interested in finding people to blame than they were finding a way to solve the problem? Will you tell me about that experience?"*

Personal Examples: Then ask clients to describe experiences in which they used blaming to try and solve their problems by saying, *"Most of us tend to blame others when we have a serious problem that we don't want to deal with at the moment. Sometimes it's just easier to deal with a problem when someone else is responsible and it's not our fault. It's also easier to avoid personal responsibility for solving the problem by blaming others for it than it is to figure out how we can take responsibility for finding a solution. On some level we want to believe that if we can convince ourselves that someone is responsible for causing the problems, the problems will either be solved or we will not have to experience any adverse consequences as a result of the problems. Have you ever used blaming to try and deal with a serious problem? Tell me about it."*

Stories and Analogies: There are a number of stories and analogies that can quickly expose blaming:

Blaming Others for Bleeding to Death:

There was a man named Jerry who had an artery in his arm cut by a mugger who slashed him with a knife. Jerry did nothing to provoke the attack. The cut artery was not Jerry's fault. It was clearly the mugger's fault. So Jerry decided to do nothing to stop the bleeding. "Why should I have to stop the bleeding," Jerry asked the paramedics, "when it's not my fault that I got cut?"

Poison Kills No Matter Who's at Fault:

There was a woman who was deliberately poisoned by her husband. When she started to feel sick after dinner, she figured what had happened. She picked up the telephone to call an ambulance but then suddenly stopped. "I didn't poison myself," she thought to herself. "This is my husband's fault. He did this to me. It's not my responsibility. Because I know it's not my fault, I don't have to do anything. The poison can't kill me now." She died later that night. She forgot that if someone poisons you and you're dying, it's better to go to an emergency room before hiring a detective to find out who poisoned you.

Blaming just isn't a very good problem-solving strategy and it can be fatal.

Challenging Blaming

Pointing Out the Problem with Using Blaming: You can show that blaming doesn't work by saying, *"Blaming your problems on others won't make them go away. You may convince yourself that your problems are someone else's fault and that you shouldn't have to deal with them, but the problems will still be there and still be as bad as they really are. Blaming others won't solve the problem or make things any better."*

Therapeutic Injunctions: Then you can give a specific therapeutic injunction against using blaming by saying, *"You don't have to invest time and energy in finding people to blame for your problems. Even if you can convince yourself you aren't to blame and convince yourself that other people are totally responsible, you will still have the problem and you will still have to deal with it. You owe yourself better than to invest time and* *energy in looking for people to blame instead of investing time and energy in looking for the best ways to solve the problem."*

Therapeutic Permission: You can give therapeutic permission to challenge blaming by saying, *"It's OK to shift your focus from finding people to blame for your problems to figuring out how to solve them!"*

Using Inner Dialogue to Challenge Blaming: The final step is to facilitate an inner dialogue between the Blaming Self (the part of the self that wants to focus on finding others to blame for the problem) and the Responsible Self (the part of the self that is willing to accept personal responsibility for dealing with the problem regardless of who is ultimately responsible).

There is an inner dissonance that underlies blaming that is caused by the conflict between the Blaming Self and the Responsible Self. Whenever one part of the personality seeks to blame others for the problem another part of the personality is usually saying, "Who cares whose fault it is? We're in trouble and we need to do something. Let's focus on how to solve the problem and figure out how to place the blame later!" This cognitive dissonance shows up in an internal argument between the two parts of the self. This cognitive dissonance can be exposed by saying, *"Even though I am hearing you say these problems are not your fault and that other people are responsible and should put things back the way they were, it seems to me there is a part of you that is at least as concerned with solving the problem as with figuring out blame. It appears there's a part of you inside that knows even if you can successfully blame someone else for your problems, you will still have to do a lot of work to solve them. Is there a part of you that sometimes thinks you are investing too much time and energy in finding people to blame and not enough time and energy trying to solve the problem? Can I talk to that part of you for a moment?"*

Once the inner conflict has been exposed it can be resolved by having an inner dialogue between both parts of the self with the goal of resolving it. One way to set up an inner dialogue is to ask the client something like this: *"Do you ever have inner conversations with yourself about who is respon-*

sible or should be blamed for this problem? Do you ever get preoccupied with finding people to blame and finding reasons that prove you are not responsible? Is there a part of you that wants to solve the problem rather than just find good reasons why it's not your fault and someone else is to blame?"

Here's an example of how it works with the minimizing denial pattern:

Therapist: Is there a part of you that is focused on finding people to blame for your problems and convincing yourself that the problems are not your fault?

Client: I guess so. The whole situation just isn't fair. I didn't do anything to cause it. Other people and situations conspired against me. I didn't deliberately create these problems. It's not my fault. Other people should be held responsible. I shouldn't be in this situation. I shouldn't be held responsible.

Therapist: So what I'm hearing you say is that a part of you spends a lot of time and energy focusing on the issue of blame. This part of you says things like, "It's not my fault! It's someone else's fault! It's not fair! I shouldn't have to deal with this! Other people should be forced to deal with these problems for me!" This part of you seems to believe that if you blame someone else for the problem, all of the negative consequences will go away. Is that correct?

Client: Yes, I guess so. I do spend a lot of time trying to figure out whose fault it is and find reasons why I shouldn't be forced to face the problems.

Therapist: Let's give that blaming part of you a name. Let's call it your Blaming Self. Is there another part of you that is more interested in solving the problem than in finding someone else to blame for having it?

Client: Well, I do want to solve the problem. Sometimes I get tired of just complaining and moaning about being a victim and waiting for others to come and deal with the situation. There's a part of me that keeps asking why I can't just handle it myself and let go of the need to blame. I keep running into the idea at my Twelve-Step meetings that says *"Turn it over."* I ask myself why I can't just forget about blaming and focus on solving the problem

Therapist: Let's call the part of you that wants to stop blaming and start focusing more time and energy on solving the problem your Responsible Self. Do you ever have inner conversations between your Blaming Self that focuses on whose fault it is and your Responsible Self that wants to move beyond blaming and focuses on finding solutions?

Client: Yes, I do.

Therapist: Can you describe a typical conversation to me? When you start thinking about the problem, which part of you kicks in first?

Client: My Blaming Self starts saying that it's not my fault. I start listing all the people who let me down. I start feeling sorry for myself and telling myself that the whole situation is not fair—that I'm just a victim.

Therapist: How does your Responsible Self respond to that?

Client: My Responsible Self tells me that blaming won't help. Like it or not I'm in trouble. The bed has been made, and no matter who made it I've got to sleep in it. My Responsible Self tells me that even if it's not my fault, I've got to clean up the mess because no one will clean it up for me.

Now the stage is set to facilitate an inner dialogue between the Blaming Self and the Responsible Self.

Teaching Self-Management for Blaming

The basic steps for teaching clients how to self-manage the blaming denial pattern are as follows:

Conscious Self-Monitoring: Make a self-monitoring card for the cognitive themes and behavioral consequences of blaming. These are: (1) Constantly thinking about whose fault the problem is; (2) constant assertions that "It's not my fault" or "I shouldn't have to be responsible"; and (3) getting into arguments with others about the issue of blame and responsibility. Then you can ask clients to do an inventory four times per day, once in the morning when they get up, once at lunchtime, once at dinnertime, and once before bed.

Recognition and Thought-Stopping: Whenever the client recognizes that they have started to blame, they need to practicing a thought-stopping method. This method involves the following steps: (1) Consciously recognizing and affirming the use of the denial pattern by saying, *"I'm starting to blame again. This isn't helpful! This won't work! I owe myself better than this";* (2) Making a conscious decision to stop this way of thinking or consciously continue by saying, *"OK, what do I want to do? I'm in the habit of blaming, but I know it doesn't do any good and just makes me feel worse. Do I want to stop blaming and start focusing on problem solving, or do I want to have an episode of intense irrational blaming to get this out of my system?"* If clients choose to have an intense episode of irrational blaming they should do so in a deliberate and conscious fashion. They should write down the names of all the people who are responsible for their problems and the reasons why these other people are responsible. Then they should write down all the reasons why it's not their fault. They should discuss this list with their therapist, at self-help group meetings, and with their sponsor. By making the blaming process conscious and deliberate, the underlying patterns of irrationality will be exposed and the secondary benefits of the irrational thinking will disappear.

If they choose to stop blaming, they *Use an Immediate Relaxation Technique* to physically relax and become mentally focused. Try to still the mind and break the thought cycle by repeating a meditation such as this: *"I am willing to let go of my need to blame. I am willing to begin to focus on what I need to do in the moment to manage this problem. I am relaxing and becoming focused on my needs in the moment."* Then they can conduct a conscious inner dialogue between the Blaming Self and the Responsible Self.

Refocusing on Problem Solving: Consciously review the written statement of the problem, the goal, and the action plan for dealing with it. Clients then need to focus on where they are in the problem-solving process by asking these questions: (1) Have I identified and clarified the problem? (2) Have I identified different alternative solutions and projected the logical consequences of each? (3) Have I selected, implemented, and evaluated the outcome of one of the alternatives? Then they can challenge themselves with the question, "Is there anything I need to do right now to deal responsibly with the core problem?"

3-6: Comparing

Clients who use comparing believe they can't have a serious problem because they know other people who have more serious problems.

Identifying Comparing

To identify comparing it is helpful to look for these things:

Gut Reactions: The primary gut reaction related to comparing is an urge to focus on someone else's problem. Even though therapists know their job is to keep clients focused on their personal problems, clients continually present interesting and compelling descriptions of other people who are worse than they are and use these extreme cases as proof that they don't have a problem.

Nonverbal Indicators: The nonverbal indicators of comparing are: (1) A "sincere" desire to help people who are sicker than they are. (Clients will start telling you about friends and relatives who "really have a serious problem." They will show genuine concern and may even ask for advice in how to help them get into treatment.); (2) Anger at being treated unfairly: (Clients often express anger at being treated unfairly by saying, *"Look at how sick these other people are. They're really bad off and yet nothing is happening to them. I'm not nearly as bad as they are, yet everyone is trying to tell me I have a serious problem and force me to do things I shouldn't have to do. It just isn't fair!");* (3) Jealousy that others who are worse aren't being held responsible for their problem (Clients also express jealousy or envy that these other people who "really have serious problems" are able to "get away with it" while they, who aren't nearly as bad off, are being forced unfairly into treatment.).

Behavioral Goals: The behavioral goal of comparing is this: To prove I don't have a problem by showing that other people have more severe problems.

Cognitive Themes and Self-Talk: The cognitive theme of

comparing is this: "It can't be a problem because others are worse off than me." When people use comparing they tend to think something like this: *"I can't possibly need to stop drinking or using drugs because I know other people who use more alcohol and drugs and who have much worse problems than I do."*

Mistaken Beliefs: The basic mistaken belief that drives comparing is this: "If someone else is worse than I am, it proves I don't have a problem." Notice that this mistaken belief will create compulsions within clients to (1) minimize or absolutely deny their own problem; (2) shift the focus of attention to someone else; and (3) invite the therapist to critically compare their problems to those of someone else.

Exposing Comparing

You can expose comparing by saying, *"What I'm hearing you say is that you can't have a problem because there are other people who have a problem that is more severe than yours. Is that correct?"*

Educating about Comparing

The next step is to educate about comparing:

Description: Name and describe comparing by saying something like this: *"What you're doing is called comparing. When people start comparing they find someone who has a problem that is more serious than their own, and then they convince themselves they don't have a problem by focusing on how minor their problem is compared to the other, more serious problem. People who use comparing to deal with problems believe that if they can find someone who is sicker than they are, their problems will be solved."*

Education: Explain what comparing is by saying, *"Comparing is a way of convincing yourself that you don't have problems by comparing yourself to people who have more serious problems so you can say to yourself, "He's so much worse, my problems don't seem so bad in comparison. I must be OK." Comparing is driven by the mistaken belief that as long as I can find someone who has a worse problem than I do, my problem will go away."*

Examples of Others: Ask the client for examples of other people who used comparing to cope with the problem by saying, *"Have you ever tried to talk with someone who had a serious problem who was more interested in telling you about other people with worse problems than they had? Will you tell me about that experience?"*

Personal Examples: Then ask clients to describe experiences when they used comparing to try and solve their problems by saying, *"Most of us tend to compare ourselves to others when we have a serious problem that we don't want to deal with at the moment. Sometimes it's just easier to say we don't have a problem because we see others who are so much sicker than we are. Have you ever used comparing to try and deal with a serious problem? Tell me about it."*

Stories and Analogies: There are stories that can quickly expose comparing:

Stanley and the Sprained Ankle:

There once was a man named Stanley who severely strained his ankle and went to the emergency room for treatment. When he got there he saw a man with a severely broken ankle. Because that man had a more severely injured ankle, Stanley just went home and said, "There's no need for me to get my sprained ankle treated because this guy has a broken ankle. Because he's so much more severely injured than I am, it means I don't have a problem at all and that I'm cured."

If I Ever Get that Bad I'll Quit:

There was a young man named Joe who went to his first drinking party and noticed a guy getting drunk and acting obnoxious. Joe said to himself, "If I ever get that drunk and obnoxious at a party, I'll recognize that I have a problem and stop drinking."

Several months later Joe got drunk and obnoxious at a party but noticed another guy who was so drunk that the host asked him to leave. Joe said to himself, "If I ever get so drunk that I get asked to leave a party, I'll recognize that I have a problem and stop drinking."

A few months later Joe got so drunk he was asked to

leave a party. He went to a bar and was drinking and socializing when he noticed a man sitting at the end of the bar drinking all by himself. Joe said, "If I ever get so bad that I have to drink all alone like him, I'll recognize that I have a problem and stop drinking."

A few months later, as he was sitting at a bar drinking alone, he looked over to the back booths and noticed a guy who was passed out with his face in a puddle of warm beer. Joe said to himself, "If I ever get so bad that I pass out with my face in a puddle of warm beer in the bar, I'll recognize that I have a problem and stop drinking."

A few months later Joe was passed out in a back booth of a bar with his face in a puddle of warm beer. When the bartender rousted him at closing time, Joe noticed another guy in the booth next to his who was being thrown unconscious out the back door because he was so drunk the bartender couldn't roust him. Joe said to himself, "If I ever get so drunk that I get thrown out in the alley because I can't be rousted at a bar's closing time, I'll recognize that I have a problem and stop drinking."

About a month later, Joe woke up in the early morning in the alley behind the bar as a street bum was trying to take his shoes. Joe saw a guy next to him who was still passed out, even though his shoes had been stolen. Joe said to himself, "If I ever get so bad that I don't wake up when some street bum tries to steal my shoes, I'll recognize that I have a problem and stop drinking."

About a month later Joe went into treatment. The therapist asked him why he was there. Joe said, "This morning I woke up in the alley behind a bar with no shoes. I looked around and didn't see anyone else I could compare myself with. So I decided I'd better get some help."

Challenging Comparing

Pointing Out the Problem with Using Comparing: You can point out that comparing doesn't work by saying, *"You know that trying to compare yourself to others in order to convince yourself you don't have serious problems won't work.*

Just because you find other people who are a lot worse off than you doesn't mean that you don't have a problem."

Therapeutic Injunctions: You say, *"You don't have to keep comparing yourself with others. You owe yourself better than that. You can figure out what's wrong and develop a plan for solving those problems!"*

Therapeutic Permission: You can give clients permission to challenge comparing by saying, *"It's OK to stop comparing yourself to others. It doesn't make any difference how much pain and problems other people are experiencing. What counts is your pain, and your problems, and what you can do to feel better and to solve those problems. It's OK to find the part of you deep inside that knows there is something wrong and wants to set it right."*

Inner Dialogue: The final step in challenging comparison is to facilitate an inner dialogue between the Comparing Self and the Objective Self. This can be done by taking your clients through the following process:

Therapist: I can see there is a part of you that likes to compare yourself with others. This part of you seems to believe everything will be OK as long as you can find someone else who is worse than you. Is that correct?

Client: Yes, I like to know where I stand. I do a pretty good job compared to some other guys I know. I think my wife and my boss should recognize that.

Therapist: Tell me about that.

Client: (The client tells about his desire to compare himself with others. He ends up talking about his resentment with being told that he has a problem when other people are so much worse than he is.)

Therapist: Do you have a name for the part of yourself that needs to know where you stand by comparing yourself to others? Why don't we call it your Comparing Self? Now let's imagine there is a part of your personality that isn't interested in how you compare to others. It's that part of you that just wants to objectively know what is happening to you, what's going right in your life, what's going wrong in your life, what's happening that makes you feel good, and what's happening that's making you feel bad. We'll call that part your Objective Self. Can you sense that part of yourself?

Client: Kind of, but it's not very clear. How can I know how well I'm doing if I don't compare myself to other people?

Now the therapist can work on giving the client a concept of using objective ethical, moral, and behavioral standards for self-evaluation instead of just looking at other people who are worse off and using that to convince themselves they are fine. Then the stage will be set to facilitate an inner dialogue between the Comparing Self and the Objective Self.

Teaching Self-Management for Comparing

To self-manage comparing, clients must be able to shift the focus from finding others who have worse problems than they do to problem solving.

Managing Comparing In Clinical Sessions: First, set up the time-out signal so that either the therapist or the client can stop the session when they notice comparing. Next, repeat the trigger questions that caused the clients to start comparing. Then keep shifting from content to process so the client can learn to change the focus from answering questions about the problem to examining the here-and-now communication process that is preventing the client from looking at the problem.

Managing Comparing in Real Life: The basic steps for teaching clients how to manage the comparing denial pattern in real life are as follows:

Step 1: *Conscious Self-Monitoring:* The self-monitoring card for comparing consists of the following: (1) Thinking and talking about other people who have more serious problems; (2) thinking that my problems are not so bad because other people have worse problems; and (3) believing I don't need treatment or recovery because other people are worse than me and they are not in treatment or recovery. Clients can use this self-monitoring card to do an inventory of their thoughts and behaviors four times per day.

Step 2: *Recognition and Thought Stopping:* Whenever clients recognize they have started to use comparing, they need to use a thought-stopping method. This means: (1) Consciously recognizing and affirming the use of the denial pattern by saying, *"I'm starting to use comparing again. This isn't helpful! I owe myself better than this."* (2) Making a conscious decision to stop this way of thinking or consciously continue by saying, *"What do I want to do? I'm in the habit of comparing myself to others when I try to deal with this problem. But I know it doesn't do any good and just makes me feel worse. I know that focusing on problem solving would be more effective. Do I want to start solving problems or do I want to have an episode of intense comparing to get this out of my system?"* If clients choose to have an intense episode of comparing, they should take a sheet of paper and make a list of all the people they can compare themselves with to prove they don't have a bad problem. Then they can take a separate sheet of paper for each person on the list, write their name on the top of the paper and divide it into two columns. In the first column they can write a list of all the reasons why they think this person is worse off than they are. In the second column they can write a list of all the ways they can see that they are similar to this person or could become as bad as they are. Then they can discuss the list with their therapist, at self-help group meetings, and with their sponsor to find new and better ways to prove that the problem really isn't as bad as everyone thinks it is. They can set the conscious goal to avoid productive problem solving and focus instead on finding people who are sicker than they are, identifying exactly how they are worse off, and in what ways they might be similar. By making the comparing process conscious and deliberate the underlying patterns of irrationality will be exposed and the secondary benefits of the irrational thinking will diminish or disappear. Then they can move to the next step.

Immediate Relaxation Techniques: Use an immediate relaxation technique to physically relax and become mentally focused. Try to still the mind and break the thought cycle by repeating a meditation such as this: *"I am aware I have a tendency to compare myself to others. I am also aware that it is my health and well-being that counts. I am willing to release and relax. I am willing to let go of all thoughts about people* *who are worse off than I am. I am willing to become aware of my problem, to evaluate how serious it is, and to figure out what I need to solve it. I am relaxing and becoming focused on my needs in this moment."*

Conscious Inner Dialogue: The next step is to conduct a conscious inner dialogue between the Comparing Self and the Objective Self. This is done in the same way as the other inner dialogues, so I won't give a detailed example.

Refocusing on Problem Solving: To consciously refocus on problem solving, clients can review a written statement of the problem, the goal, and the action plan for dealing with it. These items are often contained in the treatment plan. Clients can then evaluate where they are in the problem-solving process by asking three questions: (1) Have I identified and clarified the problem? (2) Have I identified different alternative solutions and projected the logical consequences of each? (3) Have I selected, implemented, and evaluated the outcome of one of the alternatives?

Then clients need to challenge themselves with this question: *"Is there anything I need to do right now to deal responsibly with the core problem?"* If the answer is "yes," start doing it. If the answer is "no," consciously "turn over" the need to focus on the problem by saying, "I'm doing everything I need to do to responsibly manage the problem." Then get involved in doing something else productive for your recovery, health, and well-being.

3–7: Compliance

In this section we will apply the intervention steps of the Denial Management Process (DMP) to the denial pattern called compliance. Clients who use compliance pretend to work at solving the problem in order to be left alone.

Identify Compliance

When identifying compliance it is helpful for the therapist to look for these five things:

Gut Reactions: (1) The client agrees to do something but your intuition tells you they won't follow through. (2) You have an urge to force the client to follow through by using confrontation, threats, and consequences. (3) You have an urge to give up and stop making recommendations because clients never follow through anyway.

Nonverbal Indicators: (1) Superficial agreements without a feeling of a serious commitment; (2) repeated lack of follow-through justified by excuses; and (3) superficial promises to try harder when confronted.

Behavioral Goal: To get people off my back by appearing to try and solve the problem while actually doing nothing.

Cognitive Theme and Self-Talk: The cognitive theme of compliance is: "I'll say anything you want to hear if you leave me alone."

Mistaken Beliefs: The mistaken belief that drives compliance is this: "If I can get people to leave me alone by going through the motions of solving the problem, the problem will go away." People who use compliance tend to believe the real problem is that other people are forcing them to deal with the problem. The irrationality goes like this: "The real problem really isn't the problem. The only problem I have is that people are forcing me to deal with the problem. If people would just leave me alone the problem will go away. The best way to get them to leave me alone is to convince them I'll do what they want me to do."

Exposing Compliance

You can expose compliance by saying, *"What I'm hearing you say is that you'll say anything I want to hear if I'll just leave you alone."*

Educating about Compliance

Description: You can say, *"What you're doing is called compliance. You seem to be willing to tell me anything I want to hear as long as I stay off your back. Is that correct?"*

Education: Explain compliance by saying, *"Compliance is a way of turning responsibility for your recovery over to other people by saying what they want to hear without making a decision to get actively involved in your own recovery."*

Examples of Others: Ask the client for examples of other people who used compliance to cope with the problem by saying, *"Have you ever tried to help someone who said all the* *right things, but they only went through the motions of trying to solve their problems? Tell me about that."*

Personal Examples: Ask clients to describe experiences when they complied with others in order to try to solve their problems by saying, *"Most of us tend to comply when we don't believe we have problems but others are forcing us to say that we do. Sometimes it's just easier to say what other people want to hear so they'll get off our back and leave us alone. Have you ever used compliance to try to deal with a serious problem? Tell me about it."*

Stories and Analogies: Here is a way to quickly explain the problem with denial. It's call *Good Tired and Bad Tired:*

There are two kinds of tired—good tired and bad tired. We get "bad tired" when we give in, go along, and start chasing the dreams, embracing the values, and following the agendas of other people. We get "bad tired" when we are fighting battles that aren't our own, for causes we don't really believe in, under the leadership of people we don't really respect. We can feel "bad tired" even after a day of winning, especially if the victory we fought hard to achieve violates our values or principles. When we're "bad tired," we usually see that there was very little of our own self present in what we had struggled to achieve. When we're "bad tired" it means we have complied and surrendered ourselves to the will of others.

When we're "bad tired" and our head hits the pillow at the end of the day, we toss and turn. We don't settle easy. We're tired no matter how much we rest. We drift into apathy and compliance. We feel powerless and helpless. We lose touch with our higher purpose, lapse into learned helplessness, and stop trying. We feel our energy fade away and begin to slowly die at the very core of our being. We just give in and go through the motions of doing what other people tell us to do.

When we're "good tired," we know we are working hard in our recovery by chasing our own dreams, embracing our own values, and following our own agendas. We know, at the core of our being, that we are fighting for an important cause of our own choosing. We know we are fighting for recovery in the right way, for the right reasons, and following our own inner truth.

When we're "good tired," our head hits the pillow at the end of the day and we settle easy. We sleep the sleep of the just. We can embrace ourselves and the God of our understanding and say, "Take me away, for I have done what I have been created to do!" When we're "good tired" we can rest easy and return to our lives refreshed. We can renew ourselves and return energized to our cause of our recovery.

Compliance makes us "bad tired." The only way to feel "good tired" at the end of the day is to stop complying and going along to get people off our back, and to start identifying and solving problems that are causing us to violate our own values.

Challenging Compliance

Pointing Out the Problem with Using Compliance: You can point out that compliance doesn't work by saying, *"You know that going along with others to get them off your back won't work in the long run. Compliance may seem like an effective way to stay in recovery, but it's not. Blind compliance with others forces us to disconnect from our values and our feelings. There's nothing fun about getting into recovery in order to live someone else's dreams while our dreams and ideals whither on the vine."*

Therapeutic Injunctions: You can say, *"You don't have to blindly comply with the wishes of others. You owe yourself better than that. There are other things you can do!"*

Therapeutic Permission: You can say, *"It's OK to challenge your need to comply. It's OK to find the part of you deep inside that's capable of actively collaborating and cooperating with others in your recovery, finding solid solutions to getting in recovery, and staying in recovery. It's OK to build a solid recovery program that can give you a feeling of confidence that you will be able to cope with whatever life throws* *your way without using alcohol or drugs."*

Inner Dialogue: You can facilitate an inner dialogue between the Complying Self and the Cooperative Self by using the following process:

Mistaken Beliefs: At the core of the Compliant Self is the belief: "If I can say what other people want to hear, they'll leave me alone and my problems will be solved!

Challenging Compliance

Pointing Out the Problem with Using Compliance: Show that compliance doesn't work by saying, *"It seems that you would like to believe that agreeing with everything that I say and then doing nothing is an effective way to deal with this problem. But it's not.*

"You also seem to think if I would just get off your back and leave you alone your problems will just magically disappear. Unfortunately, they won't. I'm not causing your problems. I'm just asking you to take an honest look at the problems that already exist. I want to help you figure out how to deal with those problems.

"When you tell me what I want to hear and agree to do things and then not follow through, you are just tying my hands behind my back and making it impossible for me to help you. Your compliance will only delay facing and dealing with your problems. While you're investing time and energy in these delay tactics, your problems may very well get worse."

Therapeutic Injunctions: You can say, *"You don't have to comply with everything I say or tell me things you don't really mean. You owe yourself better than that."*

Therapeutic Permission: You can say, *"It's OK to deal, to be honest, and to tell me directly what you are thinking and feeling and what you are willing and not willing to do!"*

Inner Dialogue: You can facilitate an inner dialogue between the Assertive Self and the Compliant Self. Here's an example of the process:

Therapist: Have you ever given the therapist exactly what he or she wanted without being really honest, and then relapse because you didn't face the truth?

Client: Yes, I have.

Therapist: Tell me about it.

Client: (The client tells of a past experience where they complied with their therapist's wishes and as a result failed to stay in recovery.)

Therapist: So what I'm hearing you say is that there is a part of you that wants to be compliant, do what you're told, and avoid making a personal commitment to make your recovery work. Is that correct?

Client: Yea, I guess so. Why not? You therapists are supposed to know what you're doing. I'll just do what you say. Then if it doesn't work, it's not my responsibility.

Therapist: Let's call the part of yourself that wants to comply with what others tell you whether you think it will work or not your Compliant Self. It seems that the part of your personality that wants to use compliance as a way out of trouble is in charge a lot of the time. Is that correct?

Client: Yea, I guess so. I've always believed that the best way to cope with problems is just to go with the flow. If you don't make waves, things should get better.

Therapist: Have you had any experiences where your Compliant Self was in charge?

Client: Yea, I just go along with what people expect. I tell them what they want to hear. I think that this will make things go my way.

Therapist: Can you tell me about some of these experiences? (The client explains several experiences where they used compliance to deal with a problem) Did you actually get better and stay better?

Client: I felt better for a while. I felt like I was getting one over on the therapist and the other people who were trying to help me. I felt I was taking the easy way out and that it would work. But it didn't. If those therapists were any good they wouldn't have let me get away with it.

(Note: Notice the client's attempt to shift denial patterns from compliance to blaming. Also notice that the therapist doesn't take the invitation.)

Therapist: So what I'm hearing you say is that in the past you have tried to solve your problems by complying and going through the motions without really investing yourself in the process. Is that correct?

Client: I guess so.

Therapist: You guess so, or is it true?

Client: OK, I guess it's true. My way of handling things in the past was to tell people what they wanted to hear so they would just leave me alone. I guess it didn't work very well.

Therapist: But you always tried again, didn't you? Is there a part of you deep inside that is willing to take personal responsibility and work honestly with others to get well and to stay well?

Client: Yea, there is. I'm getting sick and tired of being let down by others. Maybe it's time that I took the bull by the horns and made some decisions myself.

Therapist: Let's focus on that constructive part of your personality that is willing to work honestly with others in order to be well. Let's call that part of yourself your Assertive Self. You can sense that part of yourself, can you not?

Client: Yes, I can.

Now the stage is set to facilitate an inner dialogue between the Compliant Self that wants to go through the motions of doing what they are told and the Assertive Self that is willing to take personal responsibility for following through.

Teaching Self-Management for Compliance

The self-management of compliance involves teaching clients how to shift the focus from compliantly doing what they are told to becoming actively and creatively involved in solving their own problems.

Managing Compliance in Clinical Sessions: This is very similar to managing the other denial patterns. First, set up the time-out signal so that either the therapist or the client can stop the session when they notice it. Then repeat the trigger questions that caused the clients to start using compliance. Keep shifting from content to process so the client can learn to change the focus from talking about things that make them afraid of relapsing to identifying and solving the problems that can cause relapse.

It is important with compliant clients not to tell them what to do. They will go through the motions and then, when it fails, blame you for giving them the wrong advice. The most effective way to deal with it is to give a story or example of how someone else dealt with the problem and then ask the client if they learned anything from the story that might be helpful to them.

Managing Compliance in Real Life: The basic steps for teaching clients how to manage compliance in real life are Conscious Self-Monitoring and Recognition and Thought-Stopping.

Conscious Self-Monitoring: The self-monitoring card for compliance should contain the following indicators: (1) Losing touch with what I want to accomplish in my treatment; (2) trying to figure out what the therapist wants me to think and do; (3) telling the therapist things they want to hear even if they are not true; and (4) doing things to please the therapist even though I know they won't really be helpful. Clients can use this self-monitoring card to do an inventory of their thoughts and behaviors four times per day

Step 2: *Recognition and Thought-Stopping:* Whenever clients recognize that they have started to use compliance, they need to use a thought-stopping method. This means: (1) Consciously recognizing and affirming the use of the denial pattern by saying, *"I'm starting to use compliance again. This isn't helpful! I owe myself better than this."* (2) Making a conscious decision to stop complying and start figuring out what they really want and need to do. This starts out by asking, *"What do I want to do? I'm in the habit of dealing with my problems by complying with the wishes of others. But I know it doesn't do any good and just makes me feel worse. I know that focusing on problem solving would be more effective. Do I want to start solving problem or do I want to comply to get these people off my back?"*

If clients choose to consciously use compliance they should take a sheet of paper and divide it into two columns. In the first column they should list all the things they believe their therapist wants to hear. In the second column they should list the easiest ways they can think of to go through the motions of doing what the therapist wants. Then they can discuss the list with their therapist, at self-help group meetings, and with their sponsor.

3–8: Manipulating

When people use the manipulating denial pattern they try to get other people to do things for them that they could do for themselves.

Identifying Manipulating

When identifying manipulating it is helpful to look for these indicators:

Gut Reactions: Therapists often have the following gut reactions when dealing with clients who are manipulating: (1) Feelings of fear, apprehension, or uneasiness caused by a sense that they are being exploited or taken advantage of: They sense their clients are not being straight with them or are up to something. Upon close reflection the therapist can identify subtle threats and manipulations that communicate the unspoken message of "Do it my way or else!" (2) A sense that they are being used: Therapists begin to feel they are being set up and used by clients who have a hidden agenda and want something from them but are not coming right out and asking. (3) Feeling like a pawn or a patsy: As the manipulations of clients begin to work, the therapist feels like they are losing their power and becoming a pawn or a patsy. They have an urge to struggle to regain control, but the harder they try to control the situation the more the power seems to shift to the clients.

Nonverbal Indicators: The nonverbal indicators of manipulating are: (1) Using the superficial charm of a con artist or used car salesman: Clients will become superficially charming and go out of their way to figure out what their therapist wants and try to give it to them. This is done not with the intention of benefiting from treatment but in order to have a period of good behavior to use in a future manipulation. (2) Trying to get personal information that can be used against you later: The more the manipulative client knows about the therapist, the better their potential for deception and leverage. The less the therapist knows about the client, the less able they will be to recognize and stop the manipulations. The client will feign friendship and interest in the therapist with the goal of getting information that can later be used to force the therapist to give in. (3) Promising to meet treatment requirements, but only in exchange for some special favor. Manipulative clients believe that meeting treatment requirements is a reward they can offer their therapist in exchange for special favors or services. Their unspoken message is this: "If you treat me right I'll get well just for you. If you treat me wrong I'll relapse and make your life miserable!"

Behavioral Goals: The behavioral goal of manipulating is to force others to do things for me or to rescue me by refusing to solve my own problems. This dynamic has been called "Tyranny of the Weak." The client assumes a helpless posture, refuses to do anything to help themselves, and then demands that the therapist do it for them because they can't do it for themselves. The unspoken message is this: "How can you expect a weak and helpless person like me to do what I need to do to get well? If you don't do it for me I won't get well and it will be your fault. Do you want to be responsible for my relapse and maybe dying or killing someone else?"

Cognitive Themes and Self-Talk: People who are manipulating tend to think something like this: "I'll admit I have a problem if you handle things for me without forcing me to change."

Mistaken Beliefs: The mistaken belief that drives manipulation is, "If I can get someone else to solve my problem I won't have to do anything to solve my own problems."

Exposing Manipulating

You can expose manipulating by saying, *"What I'm hearing you say is that you'll admit you have a problem if I solve it for you without forcing you to change. Is that correct?"*

Educating about Manipulating

You can use the following steps to educate about manipulating:

Description: You can say: *"What you're doing is called manipulating. You're giving me the message that you will only admit to having the problem if I agree to solve it for you or to give you some special benefit or favor."*

Education: Explain what manipulating is by saying, *"Ma-*

nipulating is a way of convincing yourself that you don't have problems by telling yourself that you can figure out a way to get other people to solve the problems for you. The mistaken belief that drives manipulating is, 'As long as I can trick other people into taking responsibility for my problems, those problems will be solved.'"

Examples of Others: Ask the client for examples of other people who use manipulating to cope with the problem by saying, *"Have you ever tried to trick somebody else into solving your problems for you? Will you tell me about that experience?"*

Personal Examples: Then ask clients to describe experiences when they used manipulating to try to solve their problems by saying, *"Most of us try to manipulate others when we have a serious problem that we don't want to deal with at the moment. Sometimes it's just easier to put your energy into tricking other people into solving your problems for you than it is to take responsibility for solving them yourself."*

Stories and Analogies: There are stories that can quickly educate about manipulating: *The Thirsty Man Who Wanted Help:*

"There was once a man named Al who was really thirsty. He went to his therapist, explained how thirsty he was, and then asked his therapist, "Will you take a big drink of water for me?"

The therapist said, "Al, even if I tried to take a drink for you, you'd still be thirsty." Then Al accused his therapist of not wanting to help. To prove her point, the therapist took a glass of water and drank it in front of Al. Then she asked, "How do you feel?"

"You didn't do it right," Al complained. "I'm still thirsty!" His therapist tried to tell Al that there are some problems that we must solve for ourselves, and no matter how much other people try to help us, nothing will happen unless we do our part.

The Garden without a Gardner:

There was once a successful man who traveled extensively on business. He bought a new house and wanted it to have a beautiful garden. Knowing he would be gone much of the time he ordered a gardener to help him design a garden that would require minimum maintenance. When he explained that he wanted a garden that would care for itself the gardener replied, "Sir, that is impossible. If you want to have a garden there must be a gardener." There are many problems in life that cannot be delegated. If you want to have a life, you must live the life you have. This means taking responsibility for your own problems.

Challenging Manipulation

Pointing Out the Problem with Using Manipulation: You can say, *"Trying to manipulate others into solving your problems for you won't work. Eventually your manipulations will backfire and drive away the people who are willing to help you. Eventually you will have to face the reality that there are some problems you must deal with by yourself. There are some things that no one can do for us."*

Therapeutic Injunctions: You can say, *"You don't have to keep manipulating other people into solving your problems. You owe yourself better than that. You are capable of doing what needs to be done to solve your problems!"*

Therapeutic Permission: You can say, *"It's OK to stop trying to control others. You can take care of yourself. You can find the part of yourself that knows you can live your own life without having to try to control others. You can let go."*

Inner Dialogue: Then you can facilitate an inner dialogue between the Manipulative Self and the Cooperative Self. Here is an example:

Therapist: Have you ever tried to get others to solve your problems?

Client: Yes, a lot of times.

Therapist: Tell me about it. (The client explains past experiences of manipulating to try to solve problems.)

Therapist: So what I'm hearing you say is that there is a part of you that believes you must control or manipulate others or else they will control or manipulate you. Is that correct?

Client: I guess so. The best defense is a strong offense.

Therapist: So let me make sure I understand this. What

you're saying is you only see two positions in life: the victim and the victimizer, the manipulator and the person being manipulated. Is that correct?

Client: Sure. You're either on top calling the shots, or you're on the bottom doing what other people are telling you to do. That's just the way it is.

Therapist: It seems to me that the part of your personality that believes you must manipulate and be in control in order to survive is in charge a lot of the time. Is that correct?

Client: Yea, I guess so.

Therapist: Let's give it a name. Why don't we call it your Manipulative Self. You've had a lot of experiences where your Manipulative Self has been in charge, haven't you?

Client: Yea, I like to call the shots. I do my best to set it up so I can manipulate in most situations.

Therapist: Can you tell me about some of them? (The client explains several experiences where he used manipulation as a tool for recovery.) It seems that in the long run your Manipulative Self fails you. When you rely on manipulation and control to keep you in recovery, you eventually relapse. Was there ever a time when you tried to stay sober without manipulating others?

Client: I can't think of any. I don't know what would happen if I stopped trying to control others. They'd probably walk all over me.

(*Note:* Notice how, in this example, the manipulating patterns seem to be a part of a Top Dog Controlling Personality Style. This client may benefit from assessment for narcissistic, and antisocial personality traits.

Therapist: Let's imagine there is a part of your personality that can learn how to stay sober without manipulating others, a part of you that can let go of trying to be in charge. Let's call that part of you the Cooperative Self. You can sense that part of yourself, can you not?

Client: Kind of. But it's not very clear. It seems to me that approach couldn't work.

Now the therapist can work on giving the client a concept of a cooperative and collaborative self that will allow shifting between being a leader who calls the shots and being a follower who follows the lead of others without allowing themselves to become victimized. Then the stage will be set to facilitate an inner dialogue between the Manipulative Self and the Cooperative Self.

Teaching Self-Management for Manipulation

To self-manage manipulating, clients must be able to shift the focus from finding others to blame for their problems to identifying and solving their own problems.

Managing Manipulating in Clinical Sessions: To manage manipulation in clinical sessions, therapists must learn how to stay alert and vigilant yet detached. This will allow them to recognize the manipulation when it starts and refuse to feed into it. The next step is to set up the time-out signal so that either the therapist or the client can stop the session when they notice manipulating. Then repeat the trigger questions that caused the clients to start manipulating. Keep shifting from content to process so the clients can learn to change the focus from answering questions about the problem to examining the here-and-now manipulative communication process that is preventing them from seeing and solving the problem.

Managing Manipulating in Real Life: The basic steps for teaching clients how to manage manipulating in real life are as follows: The first step is *Conscious Self-Monitoring:* The self-monitoring card for manipulating should contain the following indicators: (1) thinking and planning ways to get one-up on the therapist; (2) refusing to directly ask for what you want or need; and (3) believing that the only way to get what you want or need is to trick others into giving it to you. Clients can use this self-monitoring card to do an inventory of their thoughts and behaviors four times per day.

The second step is *Recognition and Thought-Stopping:* Whenever clients recognize they have started to use manipulating, they need to use a thought-stopping method: Step 1: Consciously recognizing and affirming the use of the denial pattern by saying, *"I'm starting to manipulate again. This isn't helpful! I owe myself better than this."* Step 2: Making a conscious decision to either stop this way of thinking or consciously continue by saying, *"What do I want to do? I'm in the habit of manipulating others when I try to deal with this problem. But I know it doesn't do any good and just makes me feel worse. I know that focusing on problem solving would be more effective. Do I want to start solving the problem or do I want to try and manipulate others to solve it for me?"*

If clients choose to consciously manipulate they should take a sheet of paper and make a list of all the people they believe are gullible enough to fall for their manipulating. Then they can take a separate sheet of paper for each person on the list, write their name on the top of the paper, and divide the paper into two columns. In the first column they can write a list of all manipulative strategies they believe would work with this person. In the second column they can write a list of all the ways that trying to manipulate this person could damage the relationship or cause future problems. Then they can discuss the list with their therapist, at self-help group meetings, and with their sponsor to find new and better ways to solve their problems and get what they want.

Immediate Relaxation Techniques: Use an immediate relaxation technique to physically relax and become mentally focused.

Conscious Inner Dialogue: The next step is to conduct a conscious inner dialogue between the Manipulative Self and the Cooperative Self. This is done in the same way as the other inner dialogues, so I won't give a detailed example.

Refocusing on Problem Solving: To consciously refocus on problem solving, clients can review a written statement of the problem, the goal, and the action plan for dealing with it. These items are often contained in the treatment plan.

3–9: Flight into Health

Flight into Health is a denial pattern based on the mistaken belief that just because someone starts to feel better they are better: "When I feel good, it means that everything is going well."

Identifying Flight into Health

When identifying flight into health, look for these five things:

Gut Reactions: The client using flight into health will look and act fine. They will be in good health and good spirits. Therapists tend to feel skeptical because the client is reporting progress that is unrealistically fast or "too good to be true." Most therapists have two equally destructive gut urges: (1) to believe their client is cured and can recover without any additional help; and (2) to totally diminish their client's progress and prove to them how bad things really are by burying them in negative feedback and harsh confrontation.

Nonverbal Indicators: Clients give the following nonverbal indicators for flight into health: (1) They appear absolutely certain they are fine and that nothing will go wrong in the future. (2) They express full confidence that their problems are behind them. (3) They focus on and exaggerate positive aspects of recovery. (4) They deny or block out negative or problematic aspects of recovery.

Behavioral Goal: The behavioral goal is to get the therapist to acknowledge progress and totally block out or minimize any problems or deficient areas in recovery that need further work.

Cognitive Theme and Self-Talk: The cognitive theme of flight into health is this: "Now that I know about the problem, it will go away. I'm cured!" People using flight into health say something like this to themselves: "What a relief. I feel so much better knowing what is wrong. And because I feel better, therefore I must be better and don't need to continue my treatment!"

Mistaken Beliefs: The mistaken beliefs that drive a flight into health are: (1) Knowledge alone, without action, will solve my problem. (2) If I can look OK to others I will be OK. (3) When I feel better I am better (this is known as emotional reasoning). (4) Knowing what is wrong with me will make me better (this is called magical thinking). (5) If I can convince other knowledgeable people such as doctors and therapists that I am OK, I will be OK. (6) I should be able to get what I want without having to do what is necessary to get it!

Exposing Flight into Health

The flight into health is exposed by asking clients a series of questions and processing them carefully with active listening. Here are the questions: (1) Tell me the problems that caused you to seek treatment? (2) When did you start treatment and how many sessions have you had? (3) What makes you think you are now fully recovered and no longer need treatment or ongoing support? (4) Let's go back to each of your presenting problems, take them one by one, and list exactly what you did to resolve that problem.

Educating about Flight into Health

Description: Because people using flight into health want a quick fix, it is often helpful to expose the quick fix mentality. Here is one way to do it. You can say, *"What you're doing is called flight into health. You seem to believe that just because you're feeling better at the moment, all of your problems are solved. Is that correct?"*

Education: You can explain flight into health by saying, *"Flight into health is a way of denying that you need to use a recovery program to manage the problems that you still have. People who use flight into health focus almost entirely on how they are feeling. They refuse to think or talk about what they need to do to identify and solve the problems that can cause relapse."*

Examples of Others: You can ask for examples of other people who used flight into health by saying, *"Have you ever tried to help someone with obvious problems who told you that everything was OK because they felt better? Tell me about that."*

Personal Examples: Then you can ask clients to describe experiences when they used flight into health by saying, *"Most of us tend to use flight into health when we don't want to do the hard work necessary for managing serious problems in the long run. Sometimes it's just easier to believe that because I'm feeling better everything is fine. Have you ever used feeling good as a excuse to avoid thinking or talking about serious problems in your life? Tell me about it."*

Stories and Analogies: There are two stories that can quickly describe flight into health. The first is called *It Feels So Good to Stop:*

There was once a man who was in terrible pain because he kept hitting his fingers with a hammer until they were a mangled and bloody mess. He'd constantly complain to his therapist about the pain in his fingers, yet he kept smashing them with the hammer. One day his therapist managed to convince him to stop hitting his fingers. When he did so, a lot of the intense pain went away. His therapist then suggested he should go to the hospital emergency room to get his mangled and broken fingers treated. He said, "There's no need for that. Now that my fingers don't hurt so bad any more, I'm sure I'll be fine!"

The second story is called *The Overheating Car:*

There was a man driving an old car that he hadn't maintained very well. One day he was driving in the desert and his car started to overheat. He pulled into a gas station to see what was wrong. There was a res-taurant next to the gas station, so he parked the car and ate lunch. He then took his car over to the gas station. The car seemed to be running fine. It wasn't overheating like it had on the road. He felt better be-cause he had a good lunch and a nice rest. He decided his car was just fine and he drove off into the desert without checking it out. His car died twenty miles later and the man nearly died of thirst trying to walk back to the service station. But he sure was convinced that his car was fixed even though he didn't do much to fix it.

Challenging Flight into Health

Pointing Out the Problem with Using Flight into Health: You can say, *"I know you're starting to feel better, and that's great. I also know you would like to believe that because you're feeling better, you've solved all your problems. Unfortunately, you haven't. You still have a lot of work to do. Believing your problems are solved when they really aren't won't help. It may seem like it will, but it won't. If you act like the problems are solved while you still have the problems, you're just denying reality. You're turning off the lights rather than seeing what's really going on. Your problems won't go away, they will just sneak up and attack in the dark."*

Therapeutic Injunctions: You can say, *"You don't have to convince yourself that all your problems have been magically solved. You don't have to keep empowering the part of you that wants things to be better without doing what is necessary to make them better. You owe yourself better than that. You can do what's necessary to really solve the problem and permanently put it behind you!"*

Therapeutic Permission: You can say, *"It's OK to challenge your belief in instant recovery. It's OK to find the part of you deep inside that wants to do what is necessary to really beat this thing. It's OK to realize that lasting recovery will take consistent work over a period of time and that you will need to maintain your progress by using a life-long recovery program. That's not a pleasant truth, but it is a truth that can empower you to find long-lasting recovery one day at a time. You can find strength to face the fact that there is more work for you to do and to get started doing what you need to do to get well."*

Inner Dialogue: Now you can facilitate an inner dialogue between the Magical Self that wants an instant flight into health and the Realistic Self that realizes recovery is a long-term process that takes time and effort. This can be done by taking your clients through the following process:

Therapist: Have you ever thought you had these problems solved, stopped your treatment, and then relapsed?

Client: Yes, I have.

Therapist: Tell me about it. (The client tells of a past experience where they believed they were magically cured and stopped treatment and abandoned their recovery program.) So what I'm hearing you say is that there is a part of you that wants to be magically cured. Is that correct?

Client: Yea, I guess so. Who wouldn't? Dealing with my addiction and mental problems is tough. Who wants to believe they'll have to work this hard at it for the rest of their life?

Therapist: Let's give that part of you a name. Let's call it your Magical Self. Have you had any experiences where your Magical Self was in charge?

Client: Yea, I just think things shouldn't be so difficult. I shouldn't have to work so hard to have things go my way.

Therapist: Can you tell me about some of these experiences? (The client explains several experiences.) Did you actually get better and stay better?

Client: I felt better for a while, but it didn't last. It seems like nothing ever lasts. Why bother anyway? Maybe it's hopeless.

(*Note:* Notice the client's attempt to shift denial patterns from flight into health to strategic hopelessness. Also notice that the therapist doesn't take the invitation.)

Therapist: So what I'm hearing you say is that in the past you have tried for the quick-fix magical solution and that it didn't work very well. Is that correct?

Client: I guess so.

Therapist: You guess so, or is it true?

Client: OK, I guess it's true. My way of handling things in the past didn't really work that well. I felt better and then I stopped doing the things that made me feel better, so I got worse again.

Therapist: But you always tried again, didn't you? Is there a part of you deep inside that is willing to work hard and keep working in order to have a better life?

Client: Yea, there is. I'm getting sick and tired of taking the easy way out only to end up back where I was.

Therapist: Let's focus on that constructive part of your personality that is willing to work hard to get well and stay well. Let's call that part of yourself your Realistic Self. You can sense that part of yourself, can you not?

Client: Yes, I can.

Now the stage is set to facilitate an inner dialogue between the Magical Self that wants instant cures with little or no effort and the Realistic Self that knows recovery will take work. Remember that at the core of the Magical Self is this belief: "I should be able to get what I want without having to do what is necessary to get it!" This is the key belief that needs to be clarified and challenged to help clients break free of a flight into health.

Other Methods for Dealing with Flight into Health: There are four other ways to challenge a flight into health and to help clients identify and clarify real problems that are still present in their life. These are: (1) Review the stages of recovery and evaluate the degree of task completion of each stage. This will clearly expose the recovery tasks that have not yet been completed. (2) Review the client's past history of relapse and see if they had any flights into health in the past and explore what happened. Challenge the client to identify what is different this time. (3) Review a list of relapse warning signs and ask the client to do a current inventory to see if any of those warning signs are currently present in their life. (4) Review a list of high-risk situations and ask the client to do a current inventory to see if any of those high-risk situations are currently present in their life.

Teaching Self-Management for Flight into Health

The primary management skills for flight into health are self-monitoring activities and inventory exercises that keep the client focused on the problems and challenges of their lives. Most people who use flight into health extensively tend to exaggerate their strengths and accomplishments and minimize and avoid any problems or weaknesses. The only way to keep the pattern under control is by being constantly vigilant for hidden problems.

Conscious, daily goal setting is very important. This can be accomplished by doing a morning planning inventory and an evening review inventory. Because people using flight into health are often operating on wishful thinking rather than facts about problems and progress in recovery, they resist any objective measurement of those problems and progress.

3–10: Recovery by Fear

When people use recovery by fear they try to convince themselves and others that they could never relapse because the relapse could cause serious damage, loss, or death.

Identifying Recovery by Fear

Recovery by fear is the belief that I can scare myself into recovery and that fear alone will solve my problems and keep me in recovery. When watching for this denial pattern it is helpful to look for the following:

Gut Reactions: These gut reactions can be indicators that clients are using recovery by fear: (1) Sensing that clients fear catastrophic consequences if they relapse: You can sense the client has a fear of relapsing and see that there is good reason to be afraid because the real risk is of serious or debilitating consequences. (2) Sensing that clients have an adamant commitment to recovery: Whenever they talk about their commitment to stay in recovery, their fear goes away and is replaced by a sense of calm, relief, or confidence. Their commitment to recovery is based on emotional reasoning that goes like this: *"Because I am so afraid of the consequences of relapse, I know I will never relapse. The fact that I have no idea what I need to do in order to get into recovery and avoid relapse doesn't make any difference. All I have to do to stay in recovery is to think of the threat of consequences, feel the fear, and then everything will be fine."* (3) Feeling insecure because you can't identify a concrete recovery plan: Therapists start to feel insecure because they can't identify a concrete recovery plan that will assure that the client does what is necessary to get into recovery and avoid relapse. Therapists begin to sense the hollowness of the recovery commitment. They realize that fear alone will not keep someone in recovery. They also realize that living in continuous fear will raise stress and increase the risk of relapse. The fear itself will do nothing to teach the coping skills needed to avoid relapse.

Nonverbal Indicators: The nonverbal indicators of recovery by fear are as follows: (1) Intense fear when talking about the potential consequences of relapse. Clients become genuinely frightened when thinking about what could happen if they relapse. (2) The fear disappears when the client expresses an adamant commitment to recovery: Clients are able to manage their fear of relapse by making a strong verbal commitment to recovery. That verbal commitment, however, is not backed up by a practical recovery plan. (3) Clients get angry when you attempt to get a commitment to a specific recovery plan: They don't want to identify or solve problems. They insist that "My word is my bond" and "My promise is as good as gold." They can also invite you into a game or uproar by making statements like the following: "Are you calling me a liar? I told you I won't relapse and I'm committed to recovery. Don't you trust me? I thought we had a good relationship—now I'm not so sure!"

Behavioral Goal: The behavioral goal of recovery by fear is this: To feel better by believing that the problem will be solved if I get scared enough by the horrible consequences of not solving it.

Cognitive Theme and Self-Talk: The cognitive theme is, "I'll never do it again because I'm too scared of the consequences, and that fear will keep me in recovery." They say to themselves, "I'll never do it again because I'm too scared of the consequences. Fear alone will keep me sober and solve my problems."

Mistaken Beliefs: The mistaken beliefs that drive recovery by fear are: (1) Fear alone will solve my problems and keep me in recovery. (2) If I am scared enough about the consequences of going back to old behaviors I won't need to learn any skills or solve any problems. (3) My problems will be solved if I get scared enough about what will happen if I don't solve them.

Exposing Recovery by Fear

You can expose recovery by fear by saying, *"What I'm hearing you say is that you'll never use alcohol or other drugs again because you're too scared of the consequences and you believe the fear will keep you in recovery. Is that correct?"*

Educating about Recovery by Fear

Description: You can say, *"What you're doing is called recovery by fear. You're telling me that your intense fear of relapse will keep you in recovery. Is that correct?"*

Education: Explain what recovery by fear is by saying, *"Recovery by fear is a way of convincing yourself that you don't have to solve your problems because you could never relapse because you are so afraid of the consequences."*

Examples of Others: Ask the client for examples of other people who used recovery by fear to cope with the problem by saying, *"Have you ever tried to talk with someone who had a serious problem and they were so convinced their fear of relapse would solve all their problems that they refused to consider anything else? Will you tell me about that experience?"*

Personal Examples: Ask clients to describe experiences when they used recovery by fear to try to solve their problems by saying, *"Most of us tend to use recovery by fear when we have a serious problem that we don't want to deal with at the moment. Sometimes it's just easier to say our fear of relapse will keep us in recovery than to go through the time and effort of identifying and solving the problems that could cause us to relapse. Have you ever used recovery by fear to try to deal with a serious problem? Tell me about it."*

Stories and Analogies: There are stories that can quickly educate about recovery by fear:

Fearing the Fire Alarm:

There was a man who installed a fire alarm in his house. One night he awoke to the loud ringing of the fire alarm. He could smell smoke, but because the alarm was ringing he was sure the fire would be put out, so he went back to sleep. Firemen found his body several hours later in the burned-out shell of his house. The fire alarm is a signal that tells us something is on fire. It doesn't do anything to put out the flames. Fear is an emotional signal that tells us we are in danger. It doesn't do anything to solve the problems that are causing the danger. As a matter of fact, intense fear can make our problems worse.

Challenging Recovery by Fear

Pointing Out the Problem with Using Recovery by Fear:
You can point out that recovery by fear doesn't work by saying, *"You know that trying to scare yourself into recovery by constantly thinking about the horrible consequences that will happen if you relapse won't work in the long run. Using fear to keep yourself motivated may seem like an effective way to stay in recovery, but it's not. Fear causes stress and stress increases emotional pain, makes it harder to think clearly and use good judgment, makes our problems worse, and eventually leads to relapse. There's nothing fun about living a life of fear. We'll end up using alcohol or drugs to medicate that fear. Many people use alcohol and other drugs to handle their fear.*

Intense fear, however, can also impair judgment, cause mistakes, and immobilize people. Fear is a warning that something is wrong. Fear, however, doesn't solve anything."

Therapeutic Injunctions: You can say, *"You don't have to keep scaring yourself about how awful things will be if you relapse. You owe yourself better than that. There are other things you can do!"*

Therapeutic Permission: You can say, *"There is another way out that doesn't require you to be afraid all the time. It's OK to challenge your need to live in fear. It's OK to find the part of you deep inside that's capable of finding solid solutions to getting in recovery and staying in recovery. It's OK to build a solid recovery program that can give you a feeling of confidence that you will be able to cope with whatever life throws your way without using alcohol or drugs."*

Inner Dialogue: You can facilitate an inner dialogue between the Fearful Self and the Confident Self by using the following process:

Therapist: Will you tell me about times when you thought that being afraid of relapse would keep you in recovery? (The client tells of a past experience with using fear to keep them in recovery.)

Therapist: What I'm hearing you say is that there's a part of your personality that believes you must live in fear in order to stay in recovery. This part of you believes you must be afraid of relapse in order to avoid it. This part of you believes you must live in fear in order to stay in recovery. Is that correct?

Client: Yes, I guess so. It seems that every time I feel confident about what I'm doing, something goes wrong. Every time my fear goes away, I screw up and relapse.

Therapist: Let's call that part of your personality your Fearful Self. Before we talk about your Fearful Self, I'd like to spend a little bit of time talking about fear. Fear is a signal of possible danger. Fear alerts us to the danger. Fear cannot and does not save us from danger. We can learn to listen to the fear, identify the threat, and then do what is necessary to avoid or deal with the threat. We experience fear from time to time, and that's OK, but we don't have to live in fear in order to do the right thing.

Therapist: Now let's talk about your Fearful Self. You've had a lot of experiences where your Fearful Self has been in charge, haven't you?

Client: Yea, a lot of things have happened that have convinced me that if I ever stop being afraid I'll get into deep trouble very quickly.

Therapist: Tell me more about that. (The client explains several experiences where he used fear to stay in recovery.) It sounds like your Fearful Self fails to keep you in recovery. You get tired of being afraid all the time and eventually relapse. Was there ever a time when you stayed sober even though you weren't afraid?

Client: I can't think of any. I'd like to believe I could stay sober without being afraid all the time, but I don't know.

Therapist: Let's imagine there is a part of your personality that can learn how to stay sober without fear. A part of you that can effectively use recovery tools to stay sober without constantly fearing that you will relapse.

Client: OK.

Therapist: Let's call that part of yourself your Confident Self. You can sense that part of yourself, can you not?

Client: Kind of. But it's not very clear.

Now the therapist can work on giving the client a concept of self-confidence or self-efficacy. The therapist can help the client learn how to cope with life without fear, knowing that they can cope with any problem without having to relapse over it. This sets the stage for the inner dialogue between the Fearful Self and the Confident Self.

Teaching Self-Management for Recovery by Fear

To self-manage recovery by fear, clients must be able to shift the focus from being afraid of relapsing to identifying and solving their problems.

Managing Recovery by Fear in Clinical Sessions: To manage recovery by fear in clinical sessions, set up the time-out signal so that either the therapist or the client can stop the session when they notice it. Then repeat the trigger questions that caused the clients to start using recovery by fear. Keep shifting from content to process so the clients can learn to change the focus from talking about things that make them afraid of relapsing to identifying and solving the problems that can cause relapse.

Managing Recovery by Fear in Real Life: The basic steps for teaching clients how to manage recovery by fear in real life are as follows:

Step 1: *Conscious Self-Monitoring:* The self-monitoring card for recovery by fear should contain the following indicators: (1) Thinking and talking about things that create fear of relapse; (2) believing that I will relapse if I ever stop being afraid; and (3) refusing to focus on problem solving. Clients can use this self-monitoring card to do an inventory of their thoughts and behaviors four times per day.

Step 2: *Recognition and Thought-Stopping:* Whenever they recognize they are using recovery by fear, clients need to use thought stopping by: (1) Consciously recognizing and affirming the use of the denial pattern by saying, *"I'm starting to scare myself into recovery again. This isn't helpful! I owe myself better than this."* (2) Deciding to use or stop using denial by saying, *"What do I want to do? Recovery by fear doesn't work. Do I want to start solving the problem or do I want to try and make myself scared that I will relapse again?"*

If clients choose to consciously use recovery by fear, they should take a sheet of paper and make a list of all the ways they can make themselves afraid of relapsing. Then they can discuss the list with their therapist, at self-help group meetings, and with their sponsor to find new and better ways to solve their problems and get what they want.

3–11: Strategic Hopelessness

Clients using strategic hopelessness focus on and exaggerate feelings of helplessness and depression either to get the therapist to take care of them or to confront them so harshly they can use the confrontation as an excuse for dropping out of treatment. In this section we will apply the intervention steps of the Denial Management Process (DMP) to the denial pattern called strategic hopelessness.

Identifying Strategic Hopelessness

People pretend to be hopeless in order to convince people to stop trying to help them. When identifying strategic hopelessness it is helpful to look for these five basics:

Gut Reactions: Clients using strategic hopelessness will appear depressed and to have lost all motivation in life. There is, however, an undercurrent of manipulation. It's as if, from time to time, the depression breaks and there is a look in your client's eyes that says, "You are buying this aren't you? You believe that I'm so hopeless that you can't expect anything from me?"

Nonverbal Indicators: (1) Clients assert their helplessness so strongly that an underlying strength is evident. (2) Clients are periodically distracted from their hopelessness, catch themselves acting hopeful, and then start acting hopeless again.

Behavioral Goal: The goal of strategic hopelessness is to get therapists either to totally take care of them or to confront them so harshly they can use the confrontation as an excuse for dropping out of treatment. These clients give therapists the invitation to give up on them because things are so bad there is nothing that can be done. This behavior invites the therapist to use one of two extreme responses: (1) *Caretaking:* Therapists who move into caretaking accept their clients' behavior at face value, assume they are too depressed and debilitated to function, and begin taking care of things for their clients instead of insisting their clients take responsibility for doing things for themselves. This fosters a dependency relationship that rewards clients for being helpless and depressed, and as a result the strategic hopelessness is reinforced. (2) *Confronting:* Therapists who move into confronting refuse to accept that their clients are depressed and debilitated. They see their clients' behavior as a total manipulation and get mad at clients for trying to manipulate them. These therapists can then channel their anger into confrontation strategies. The end result of the confrontation is that clients either prove to the therapist they are truly debilitated by getting worse, or clients drop out of treatment using the harsh confrontation of the therapist as an excuse.

So be alert for the gut reaction that says, "This client appears depressed, but something is wrong and I'm not sure what." Also be alert for the urges to accept one or both invitations: the invitation to enable ("This client is so helpless that I must do what is necessary to make him or her well!") or the invitation to confront ("This client is pretending to be worse off than he or she really is and I won't let them get away with it. I'll teach them a lesson by forcing them to be responsible for their recovery whether they want to be or not.")

Cognitive Theme and Self-Talk: People using strategic hopelessness play hopeless in order to convince others to stop trying to help. The cognitive themes are: (1) "I've tried everything and nothing has worked!" (2) "I'm hopeless and you can't help me, so leave me alone." and (3) "How can you expect a helpless and hopeless person like me to face my problems and deal with them?"

Mistaken Beliefs: The primary mistaken beliefs associated with strategic hopelessness are: (1) "I am helpless—there is nothing I can do to make things better;" (2) "I am hopeless—there will never be anything that I can do to make things better;" (3) "There is no way out—it will always be like this;" (4) "The only real problem I have is that you are messing up my life by trying to help me;" (The client is telling you that their problems aren't the real problem. You, as their therapist, are their real problem. It is your efforts to get them to look at their real problem that is messing them up. If you would just leave them alone their problems would be solved.); and (5) "If I can convince you I'm hopeless you will leave me alone and my problems will be solved." People who initially use compliance ("I'll pretend to do what you want in order to get you to leave me alone") will often shift into strategic hopelessness ("I've tried to do everything you suggested and nothing has worked. I'm hopeless so leave me alone and let me suffer in peace.").

Exposing Strategic Hopelessness

Exposing strategic hopelessness forces therapists to walk a fine line between confrontation and enabling. It is important to take the depression and hopelessness seriously by evaluating for depression and suicidal tendencies. If needed, take all necessary suicide precautions.

Then expose the client's feelings of helplessness and hopelessness without directly confronting them and without encouraging them. Experiment with the paradoxical intervention of tentatively agreeing with their self-assessment by saying something like this:

Therapist: What I'm hearing you say is that you feel *completely* helpless and hopeless. Is that correct? (Emphasize the word completely.)

Client: I don't know. Things are really bad.

Therapist: I'm hearing that things are *really* bad. I'm also hearing you say that these *really bad* things are making you *completely* helpless. Is that correct?

Client: Well, things are pretty bad!

Therapist: You're saying that things are pretty bad, but what I'm hearing you say is that things are worse than pretty bad. I'm hearing you say that things are terrible, and awful, and that you're *completely* helpless and can't do anything. Am I hearing you correctly?

Client: Well, not exactly. Things are pretty bad. But I don't know if I'm completely helpless.

Therapist: Really. You're not completely helpless? Tell me more about that.

Now you can ask clients to tell you about all of the problems and situations they are experiencing that are beating them down and making them feel helpless and hopeless, and ask them to write them down in a list. Here's an example:

Therapist: I'm sorry. I must have misunderstood you. Didn't you say earlier that you tried *everything* and nothing worked? Did I hear you correctly?

Client: Well, I have tried everything and nothing has worked!

Therapist: I see. Could you tell me about the things you have tried? Perhaps we could make a list.

Client: What good would that do?

Therapist: I don't know. I just think it would help me to know about all of the things you've tried that have failed. Would you do it for me, to humor a crazy old therapist?

As the client develops the list, watch for the cognitive dissonance between the *hopeless part of them* that believes they are helpless and have tried everything and the *hopeful part of them* that still believes or wants to believe there might be something they could do to make things a little bit better. You can say something like this:

Therapist: I can see there is a big part of you that feels helpless and hopeless. Is that correct?

Client: Yes, it is.

Therapist: I can also see there is a part of you that wants to believe there might be something else you can do that might make things better. Is that right?

Client: I'm not so sure about that!

Therapist: Of course you're not. But notice that when you say you're not so sure, what you're actually saying is that there is a part of you that has at least a tiny little bit of hope.

Educating about Strategic Hopelessness

Description: You can say, *"What you're doing is called strategic hopelessness. You believe you've tried everything and that you're helpless and hopeless. If it's really hopeless, then you won't have to work at your recovery. You can just give up."*

Education: You can explain strategic hopelessness by saying, *"Strategic hopelessness is a way of avoiding responsibility for working to recover by convincing yourself that there is no way you could ever get better no matter what you did. People who use strategic hopelessness focus almost entirely on what they can't do and what won't work. They refuse to think or talk about what they can do and what could work."*

Examples of Others: You can ask for examples of other people who used strategic hopelessness by saying, *"Have you ever tried to help someone with some problems who told you they had tried everything and nothing had worked, so it made no sense to try again? Will you tell me about that?"*

Personal Examples: Then you can ask clients to describe experiences when they used *strategic hopelessness* by saying, *"Most of us tend to use strategic hopelessness when we feel overwhelmed by our problems and so exhausted that* *we just don't want to work at it anymore. Sometimes it's just easier to believe that if we give up and stop trying we'll feel better and everything will be fine. Have you ever felt that way? Tell me about it."*

Stories and Analogies: There are a number of stories that can quickly explain strategic hopelessness. One story is called *The Suicidal Man Who Wanted to Live:*

There was a man with a huge belly who was admitted to a psychiatric unit with a bandage on his belly from a suicide attempt. His therapist asked him why he tried to kill himself by cutting open his stomach with a razor blade. The patient said: "I'm not that stupid. I wanted to die so I tried to slash my wrist with the razor blade. At the last minute I flinched, pulled my wrist away, and cut my stomach. "Was there a part of you that wanted to live?" the therapist asked. "Was there a part of you that wanted to have hope? Was it that part of you that made you pull away at the last minute?"

Here is another story that has worked well:
It Hurt Too Bad to Die.

There was a man named Jack who was in treatment for addiction. Jack also had a bad heart. One night Jack started to feel that it was useless to try to recover again because he had failed so many times in the past. Jack left treatment to commit suicide. He left a suicide note that said he was hopeless and that he was going to go and get a gun, drive his car out in the country to where his body would never be found, and kill himself. Three days later Jack called his therapist from an intensive cardiac care unit. "What happened?" his therapist asked. "I was driving out in the country to kill myself," Jack said, "and I started to have a heart attack. So I went to the emergency room to get help. "If you wanted to kill yourself," his therapist asked, "Why did you go to the emergency room? Why didn't you just pull off the road and die?" Jack thought about it for a moment and said, "It hurt too much to want to die! It wasn't until I was looking death in the face that I realized how much I wanted to stay alive."

Challenging Strategic Hopelessness

Pointing Out the Problem with Using Strategic Hopelessness: The first thing to do when challenging strategic hopelessness is to point out that it doesn't work. There is no way that using strategic hopelessness could ever produce a positive outcome. This can be done by saying something like this: *"You know that believing that you're hopeless won't help. It may seem like the easy way out but it's not. If you give up you'll just get more depressed, feel worse, and become more powerless. There's nothing fun about being depressed and helpless. The answer isn't to do things that make it worse."*

Therapeutic Injunctions: The second thing to do is to give a specific therapeutic injunction against using strategic hopelessness as a problem-solving strategy. This can be done by saying something like this: *"You don't have to keep focusing on your helplessness and hopelessness. You don't have to keep empowering the part of your personality that wants you to give up. You owe yourself better than that. There are other things that you can do!"*

Therapeutic Permission: You can say, *"It's OK to challenge your hopelessness. It's OK to find the part of you deep inside that wants to beat this thing. It's OK to try again. You can find the strength to challenge your hopelessness. You can learn the skills to do it. I'll be there to help you. I'll show you how to find other people who can help you. You don't have to face it alone. It's OK to get well again."*

Inner Dialogue: The final step in challenging strategic hopelessness is to facilitate an inner dialogue between the Hopeful Self and the Hopeless Self. This can be done by taking your clients through the following process. First, ask your clients, *"Have you ever been down and out and felt like giving up?"* If they answer "yes," say, *"Tell me about it!"* Then use active listening to get a detailed description. What follows is a simulated script of the rest of the clinical interaction:

Therapist: So what I'm hearing you say is that there is a part of you that feels pretty hopeless. Is that correct?

Client: Yea, I guess so. You know. Sometimes I just ask myself, "Why bother?"

Therapist: Do you have a name for that part of yourself?

Client: A name for it. What do you mean?

Therapist: Everyone has different parts of their personality. Some of those parts invite us to think thoughts that make us feel hopeless. Other parts invite us to think things that make us feel hopeful. We often don't recognize these parts of our personality because we've never taken the time to think about what goes on inside us or to name the different parts of our personality. Without naming them, we can't directly deal with them. And if we can't deal with them, they can end up controlling us. The first step to getting free is to name the part of you that is in charge. So, let's give it a name. Why don't we call it your Hopeless Self or the Hopeless Me?

Client: OK.

Therapist: It seems to me that your Hopeless Self is in charge of your thinking a lot of the time. Is that correct?

Client: Yea, I guess so. A lot of things happen that make me feel pretty helpless and hopeless.

Therapist: Will you tell me about some of them? (Explains several experiences where he felt helpless and hopeless.) Did you survive those experiences?

Client: What do you mean? I'm here. Of course I survived!

Therapist: Are you saying you've been in situations that seemed hopeless, you felt there was no way out, but you somehow managed to survive?

Client: I guess so.

Therapist: You guess so, or did you in fact survive?

Client: Yea, I survived. I got through a lot of things in the past.

Therapist: In those past situations what did you do that allowed you to survive the period of hopelessness? What part of you deep inside allowed that to happen?

Client: I'm not sure. I never thought about it before.

Therapist: Well, let's think about it now. Is there a part of your personality that allowed you to survive situations in the past that made you feel hopeless?

Client: Yea, there is. I'm a survivor. I guess I've always known that. It's just a shame there is so much in my life that I have to survive. It's not fair.

Therapist: No, it's not fair. But I want to focus on that hopeful part of you that allows you to survive. Can we do that?

Client: OK.

Therapist: Let's call that hopeful part of yourself that has allowed you to survive your Hopeful Self. You can sense that part of yourself, can you not?

Client: Yes, I can.

Now the stage is set to facilitate an inner dialogue between the Hopeful Self and the Hopeless Self. This often leads clients to reconnect with the hopeful part of their personality. They also learn the exact self-talk that is used by their Hopeless Self and learns how to challenge those irrational ways of thinking.

Teaching Self-Management for Strategic Hopelessness

The self-management skills for dealing with strategic hopelessness involve the same skills needed in treating a severely depressed client: (1) Learning to detach from and objectively evaluate the severity of the helplessness, hopelessness, and depression; (2) identifying the situations that are creating and maintaining the helplessness, hopelessness, and depression; (3) identifying the thoughts that make the helplessness, hopelessness, and depression worse; (4) identifying a past experience where you felt helpless, hopeless, and depressed but somehow managed to survive and become at least somewhat hopeful again (this must include identifying and listing the things that happened and what you did that allowed you to survive); and (5) setting short-term, concrete behavior goals for high-risk situations that allow you to do things on a routine basis using your therapy program to help you.

3–12: Democratic Disease State

Clients using the democratic disease state believe they have an inherent right to drink, drug, be mentally ill, and destroy their own life and the lives of others.

Identfying Democratic Disease State

To identify the democratic disease state it is helpful to look for the following:

Gut Reactions: People using the democratic disease state present themselves as persons who are entitled to drink, drug, be mentally ill, and destroy their own life and the lives of others. There is either an overt or covert sense of superiority and arrogance. The client's behavior is saying, "I'm above the rules. I'm immune from the consequences. I'd rather be dead than to knuckle down to what others want me to do. It's better to rule in hell than to serve in heaven. So leave me alone!" You may feel the urge to argue and try to convince clients they don't have the right to hurt themselves and others. This, of course, would be a big mistake.

Nonverbal Indicators: The nonverbal indicators of the democratic disease state are behavioral cues related to putting themselves one-up while putting others one-down and detaching from all logic and all interest in anyone except themselves. Many people who extensively use the democratic disease state have antisocial and narcissistic personality traits.

Behavioral Goals: The behavioral goals of the democratic disease state are: (1) To convince others to leave them alone by invoking their right to be addicted, mentally ill, and to die; (2) to deny that they are hurting other people, including people they love, by doing what they are doing; and (3) to prove that nobody really cares about them and that there is nothing worth living for.

Cognitive Theme and Self-Talk: The cognitive theme is, "I have the right to drink, use drugs, be addicted, be mentally ill, destroy my life, and die. It's none of your business. You don't have the right to stop me because I'm only hurting myself! So leave me alone."

Mistaken Beliefs: The mistaken belief that drives the democratic disease state is this: "I have the right to drink, drug, be mentally ill, and destroy my own life and the lives of others. Because I have this right I should be left alone to die in peace." The mistaken belief is that addiction or uncontrolled mental illness will end in a peaceful death. They don't. Addiction and untreated mental illness are two of the most painful and humiliating ways to die.

Exposing Democratic Disease State

You can expose the democratic disease state by saying, *"What I'm hearing you say is that you have the right to drink, use drugs, and destroy your life. It doesn't matter how the lives of those involved with you will be affected. Everyone should just leave you alone to die in peace. Is that correct?"*

Educating about Democratic Disease State

Description: You can say, *"What you're doing is called the democratic disease state. You believe that you have the right to drink, drug, be mentally ill, and destroy your own life and the lives of others. You believe that other people should leave you alone to die in peace."*

Education: You can explain the democratic disease state by saying, *"The democratic disease state is a way of avoiding responsibility for working to recover by convincing yourself that you have a right to die no matter what your death would do to other people. People using the democratic disease state believe that it will be easier to die from addiction than to keep living and face the job of recovery."*

Examples Of Others: You can ask for examples of other people who used the democratic disease state by saying, *"Have you ever tried to help someone with some problems who told you they had a right to their problems and really didn't care if they died and destroyed others in the process? Will you tell me about that?"*

Personal Examples: Then you can ask clients to describe experiences when they used the democratic disease state by saying, *"It's easy to believe that we have a God-given right to have our problems. Have you ever felt that people should just ignore your problems, leave you alone, and let you destroy yourself without making such a fuss?"*

Challenging Democratic Disease State

Logical Consequences: The first thing to do is to point out the logical consequences of the democratic disease state and to show that it doesn't work. You can say, *"Believing you have a right to destroy yourself won't help you or anyone else. It may* *seem like the easy way out but it's not. If you assert your right to destroy yourself you probably will, and it won't be a pleasant process. There's nothing fun about slowly destroying yourself by letting an addiction or a mental disorder spiral out of control and slowly kill you. Like it or not, your addiction or mental illness will continue to get worse and cause you to suffer more unless you face it and do what is necessary to treat it."*

Therapeutic Injunctions: Next you can give a therapeutic injunction against using the democratic disease state by saying, *"You don't have to keep focusing on your right to destroy yourself by letting your addiction or mental illness control your life. You owe yourself better than that. There are other things you can do!"*

Therapeutic Permission: Then you can give therapeutic permission to challenge the democratic disease state and to find the part of the self that is capable of rising above the right to self-destruction and thereby find a way to exercise the right to live a meaningful and satisfying life. You can say, *"It's OK to challenge your belief in your right to destroy yourself. It's OK to find the part of you deep inside that realizes that destroying yourself is not a solution. It's OK to want to find hope and the strength to face your problems and to set things right. You owe it to yourself to assert your right to solve your problems and live your life."*

Inner Dialogue: The final step in challenging the democratic disease state is to facilitate an inner dialogue between the Destructive Self (the part of the self asserting the right to destroy myself) and the Constructive Self (the part of the self capable of asserting the right to live productively). Here is a transcript of a clinical session that shows how to do this:

Therapist: Have you ever let your self-destructive urges get control of you?

Client: If you mean have I felt like this before, the answer is yes!

Therapist: Will you tell me about it? (The client then tells of a past experience when they asserted their right to be self-destructive based on the belief that drinking themselves to death was the best way out.) So what I'm hearing you say is that there is a part of you that is pretty self-destructive and believes you have the right to destroy yourself. Is that correct?

Client: Yes. I don't have to get well if I don't want to. I have a right to just give up and stop trying.

Therapist: Do you have a name for that part of yourself?

Client: A name for it. What do you mean?

Therapist: Everyone has different parts of their personality. Some of those parts invite us to think that we have a right to destroy ourselves. Other parts within us invite us to think in a way that makes us realize that we have the right to live our lives in a meaningful and satisfying way and that we don't have to surrender to our self-destructive urges. We often don't recognize these parts of our personality because we've never taken the time to think about what goes on inside of us. We've never taken the effort to notice the different parts of our personality or to name them. Without naming them, we can't deal directly with them. And if we can't deal with them they can end up controlling us. The first step to getting free is to name the part of you that is in charge. Do you have a destructive part of yourself?

Client: Yea, I guess so.

Therapist: Let's give it a name. Let's call it your Destructive Self. You've had a lot of experiences where your Destructive Self has been in charge, have you not?

Client: Yea, I don't like people telling me what to do. If something is hopeless, I don't want anyone to tell me I have to fight back. Why bother? It's my right to live. It's my right to die. It's a free country. So to answer your question—yes, this part of me is in charge a lot.

Therapist: What part of you? (The therapist then works with the client to actually use the term Destructive Self. Most clients don't want to name the part of them they are putting in charge of their future.) Can you tell me about some experiences you have had when your Destructive Self was in charge? (The client explains several experiences that occurred when his or her Destructive Self was in charge.) Did you survive those experiences?

Client: What do you mean? I'm here. Of course I survived!

Therapist: So what I'm hearing you say is that in the past you have been in situations where you put your Destructive Self in charge, but you didn't totally self-destruct. Is that correct?

Client: Well, I guess so.

Therapist: Why do you suppose you survived and got better even though you put your Destructive Self in charge? You did survive, did you not?

Client: Yes, I did.

Therapist: Was there another part of you at work that helped you survive?

Client: I don't know. I've never thought about it before. Maybe there was. It seems like there almost had to be.

Therapist: Well, let's think about it now. Is there a part of your personality that wants you to exercise your right to stay alive and live productively even though it will mean doing things that are hard?

Client: I guess there is.

Therapist: Let's call that part of you that wants to exercise your right to live your Constructive Self. You can sense that part of yourself, can you not?

Client: Yes, I can.

Now the stage is set to facilitate an inner dialogue between the Constructive Self and the Destructive Self. Normally at the core of the Destructive Self are three core beliefs: (1) *"I have the right to destroy myself and to hurt those who love me;"* (2) *"No one has the right to stop me;"* and (3) "*No one has the right to hold me accountable for my behavior!"* These are the three key beliefs that need to be clarified and challenged to help clients break free of the democratic disease state.

Teaching Self-Management for Democratic Disease State

The self-management skills for dealing with the democratic disease state are as follows: (1) Learning to recognize the underlying arrogance, anger, and entitlement; (2) identifying the situations where the democratic disease state are effective in manipulating others through guilt; (3) identifying the thoughts that make the tendency toward passive self-destruction worse; (4) identifying a past experience where they used the democratic disease state but somehow managed to survive (This must include identifying and listing the things that happened and what they did that allowed them to survive); and (5) setting short-term concrete, behavior goals for high-risk situations that allow them to do things on a routine basis using their therapy program to help.

3–13: Denial Strategies

Before we leave our detailed discussion of how to manage individual denial patterns, I want to focus on the natural tendency that most clients have to move from one denial pattern to another. Many clients start out with avoidance *("I'll talk about anything except the real problem!")*. When the therapist keeps a relentless focus on identifying and clarifying what is wrong, clients tend to get angry and move into absolute denial by asserting *"No, not me. I don't have a problem!"*

This outward assertion is usually accompanied by an inner conflict with the part of the self that knows they do have a problem. When this inner conflict is exposed the absolute denial collapses and the person moves into minimizing by saying, *"Alright, so I do have a problem, but it's not that bad. Everyone is making the problem seem worse than it is."*

When the therapist calmly asks the client to evaluate how bad the problem is by using a ten-point scale and giving the client feedback, many clients start to rationalize by saying, *"Yes, I have a problem, but there is a good reason for it."* As the therapist probes to identify and clarify those "good reasons," the client often moves into blaming and the search begins for a scapegoat who caused the problem.

Once you understand that clients have a natural tendency to progress through the denial patterns, it is possible to move directly from absolute denial to minimizing in the following way. When clients start to deny or minimize a problem, just say, *"I bet you have a good reason for thinking that!"* The client generally says, *"Yes, I do!"* Then you say, *"Tell me about it!"* The client will then begin presenting the rationalizations.

In response the therapist can say, "*It sounds to me like this isn't all your fault. Does a part of you think that someone else might be to blame?*" This will expose the tendency to blame.

All clients have these tendencies. They constantly run through the entire list of denial patterns in their head. They are locked into the denial process to the point of being obsessed with it. The denial itself can become a self-reinforcing pattern of irrational thinking that is more destructive than the problem that is being denied.

The only way to manage the denial is to expose these thought patterns to your clients, directly challenge them through education, rational confrontation, and self-management training, and then put the focus of the therapy where it belongs—on identifying and solving the core problems that are destroying your clients' lives.

Bibliography

1. Addis-E-A. Alcoholic: "But I Haven't Got a Problem, Doctor.". AUST. FAM. PHYSN, 8: 976-981, 1979. (056422)

2. Allan, C.A. Acknowledging alcohol problems: The use of a visual analogue scale to measure denial. Journal of Nervous and Mental Disease, 179(10):620–625, 1991. (113004)

3. Allan, C.A. Does denial matter? A scale to measure denial and its links with attendance for treatment. 36th International Congress on Alcohol and Drug Dependence (*36eme Congres International sur l'Alcoolisme et les Toxicomanies*), Vol. I, Glasgow, Scotland, 16–21 Aug 1992, 861 p (pp 632–634) (123935)

4. Altman-H; Evenson-R; Cho-d W. Predicting length of stay by patients hospitalized for alcoholism or drug dependence. J. Stud. Alc., 39:197–201, 1978. (033581)

5. Amodeo, M.; Liftik, J. Working through denial in alcoholism. Families in Society: Journal of Contemporary Human Services, 71(3):131–135, 1990. (107440)

6. Barnes-H-N. Presenting the diagnosis: Working with denial. In: H.N. Barnes, M.D. Aronson, and T.L. Delbanco (Eds.), Alcoholism: A guide for the primary care physician. Frontiers of Primary Care Series, New York, NY: Springer-Verlag, 1988. 252 p. (pp 59–65). (103832)

7. Batel, P.; Tkoub, E.M.; Pessione, F.; Lancrenon, S. *Essai d'evaluation des attitudes de deni en clinique alcoologique* (Evaluation of attitudes of denial in clinical alcohology) Alcoologie, 21(1):35–42, 1999. (149118)

8. Bateman-Nils-I. Study of Socially Adaptive Aspects of Alcoholic Denial. Ann Arbor, MI: University Microfilms, 1965. (010088)

9. Baughan D.M. Crisis precipitation in alcoholism. Western Journal of Medicine, 145(5):680–681, 1986. (089217)

10. Belkin, B.M.; Miller, N.S. Agreement among laboratory

tests, self-reports, and collateral reports of alcohol and drug use. Annals of Clinical Psychiatry, 4(1):33–42, 1992. (123648)

11. Berry, G.W. Effect of denial on two alcoholism screening measures. Dissertation Abstracts International, 52(1):510–B, 1991. (112031)

12. Bishop, D.R. Clinical aspects of denial in chemical dependency. Individual Psychology, 47(2):199–209, 1991. (115692)

13. Blanchard, H.B., Jr. Using three measures of addiction severity to predict treatment continuance of outpatients and counselor-evaluated prognosis of post-treatment abstinence of inpatients. Dissertation Abstracts International, 56(9):5159–B, 1996. (132643)

14. Breuer, H.H.; Goldsmith, R.J. Interrater reliability of the Alcoholism Denial Rating Scale. Substance Abuse, 16(3):169–176, 1995. (129764)

15. Brunson, M.D. Primary and secondary alcoholics and their use of denial and repression. Dissertation Abstracts International, 55(7):3006B, 1995. (126485)

16. Burling-T-A; Reilly-P-M; Moltzen-J-O; Ziff-D-C. Self-efficacy and relapse among inpatient drug and alcohol abusers: A predictor of outcome. Journal of Studies on Alcohol, 50(4):354–360, 1989. (104048)

17. Burns-J-D. Effects of self-efficacy training on coping skills of alcoholics. Dissertation Abstracts International, 45(5):1580B, 1984. (083537)

18. Cecero, J.J.; Karp, S.A. Denial and self denigration in the draw-a-person profiles of alcoholics. Current Psychology, 15(3):254–257, 1996. (152686)

19. Chambers, G.T. Relationship of cognitive impairment and denial to alcohol treatment progress. Dissertation Abstracts International, 50(7):3147–B, 1990. (106943)

20. Clark-D-E; McCarthy-E; Robinson-E. Trauma as a symptom of alcoholism. Annals of Emergency Medicine, 14(3):274, 1985. (076866)

21. Conigliaro, J.; McNeil, M.; Kraemer, K.; Conigliaro, R.; Joswiak, M.; Maisto, S. Are patients diagnosed with alcohol abuse in primary care ready to change their behavior? JGIM, 12(suppl 1):113, 1997. (142610)

22. Criddle-W-D. Rational emotive psychotherapy in the treatment of alcoholism. In: N.J. Estes and M.E. Heinemann, Alcoholism: Development, Consequences, and Interventions. Second Edition, St. Louis, MO: C.V. Mosby Company, 1982. 385 p. (pp. 339–348). (090771)

23. Davis, S.K.; Lanz, J.B. Perceptions of denial among pregnant and parenting chemically dependent women enrolled in treatment. Substance Use and Misuse, 34(6):867–885, 1999. (148455)

24. Dicicco-L; Unterberger-H; Mack-J-E. Confronting Denial: An Alcoholism Intervention Strategy. Psychiat. Ann., N.Y., 8 (No. 11): 54–64, 1978. (038796)

25. Duffy, J.D. Neurology of alcoholic denial: Implications for assessment and treatment. Canadian Journal of Psychiatry, 40(5):257–263, 1995. (128610)

26. Eckardt-M-J; Rawlings-R-R; Martin-P-R. Biological correlates and detection of alcohol abuse and alcoholism. Progress in Neuro-Psychopharmacology and Biological Psychiatry, 10(2): 135–144, 1986. (091849)

27. Edelman-S-E. Alcoholic denial. Psychiatric Annals, 9(8):387–388, 1979. (044615)

28. Fewell-Christine-H; Bissell-Leclair. Alcoholic Denial Syndrome: An Alcohol-Focused Approach. social casework, 59(1):6–13, 1978. (032061)

29. Fals-Stewart, W.; Shanahan, T.; Brown, L. Treating alcoholism and substance abuse: A neuropsychiatric perspective. Psychotherapy in Private Practice, 14(1):1–21, 1995. (139376)

30. Forman-R-F. Interventions: Some guidelines for performing a denial-ectomy. Alvernia College Addictionary, 2(1):1–4,1986. (092321)

31. Forrest, Gary G., Confrontation in Psychotherapy with the Alcoholic, Learning Publications, Inc., Palm Beach, FL 1982

32. Galanter-M. Religious conversion: An experimental model for affecting alcoholic denial. In: M. Galanter, Ed., Currents in Alcoholism: Treatment and Rehabilitation and Epidemiology. Volume VI, New York, NY: Grune & Stratton, 1979. 345 p. (pp. 69–78) (046339)

33. Galanter-M; Sofer-S-C. Systems view of treatment mo-

tivation. In: F.A. Seixas, Ed., Currents in Alcoholism: Psychiatric, Psychological, Social, and Epidemiological Studies. Volume IV, New York: Grune & Stratton, 1978. 498 p. (pp. 139–152) (034567)

34. Gibbs, V. Investigation of ego defenses in recovering alcoholics. Dissertation Abstract International, 54(9):4901B, 1994. (122452)

35. Goldsmith-R-J; Green-B-L. Rating scale for alcoholic denial. Journal of Nervous and Mental Disease, 176(10):614–620, 1988. (101480)

36. Gorski, Terence. Denial Process and Human Disease. 1(5):1–7, 1976. (038636)

37. Gorski, Terence. Denial Patterns: A System for Understanding the Alcoholic's Behavior. 1(6):1–6, 1976. (038637)

38. Grant, B.F. Barriers to alcoholism treatment: Reasons for not seeking treatment in a general population sample. Journal of Studies on Alcohol, 58(4):365–371, 1997. (140489)

39. Griffin-P-P. Therapeutic processes affecting denial in alcohol groups. Dissertation Abstracts International, 49(10):4540–B, 1989. (103225)

40. Griffith-P-R. "Learned helplessness" and ego defense mechanisms in alcohol treatment. Employee Assistance Quarterly, 1(4):87–92, 1986. (087742)

41. Hoffman, N.G.; Ninonuevo, F.G. Concurrent validation of substance abusers self-reports against collateral information: Percentage agreement vs. k vs. Yule's Y. Alcoholism: Clinical and Experimental Research, 18(2):231–237, 1994. (123116)

42. Howard, M.O.; Donovan, D.; Morse, R.M.; Flavin, D.K. Definition of alcoholism. JAMA : Journal of the American Medical Association, 269(5):586–587, 1993. (117717)

43. Kofoed, L. Engagement and persuasion. In: N.S. Miller, Ed. Principles and Practice of Addictions in Psychiatry, Philadelphia, PA: W.B. Saunders Company, 1997. 567 p. (pp. 214–220) (137785)

44. Krueger-D-W. Neurotic behavior and the alcoholic. In: E. Pattison, and E. Kaufman, Eds., Encyclopedic Handbook of Alcoholism, New York, NY: Gardner Press, 1982. 1230 p. (pp. 598–606). (066872)

45. Kufner-H. Zur Frage von Verleugnungstendenzen bei Alkoholabhangigen (Problem of denial tendency among alcoholics). Drogalkohol, 6(3):21–36, 1982. (067364)

46. Landeen-R-H. Will power and denial: Clinical findings about these pervasive concepts. In: M. Galanter, Ed., Currents in Alcoholism: Biomedical Issues and Clinical Effects of Alcoholism. Volume 5, New York, NY: Grune & Stratton, 1979. 378 p. (pp. 301–307). (080337)

47. Lederer, G.S. Use of denial and its gender implications in alcoholic marriages. In: J.A. Lewis, Ed., Addictions: Concepts and Strategies for Treatment, Gaithersburg, MD: Aspen Publishers, 1994. 393 p. (pp. 263–275) (123871)

48. Lehman-C-V. Alcoholic bottom: Problem recognition and help seeking by alcoholics. Dissertation Abstracts International, 45(7):1992–A, 1985. (083979)

49. Levy, M. Psychotherapy with dual diagnosis patients: Working with denial. Journal of Substance Abuse Treatment, 10(6):499–504, 1993. (121374)

50. Loethen, G.J.; Khavari, K.A. Comparison of the Self-Administered Alcoholism Screening Test (SAAST) and Khavari Alcohol Test (KAT): Results from an alcoholic population and their collaterals. Alcoholism: Clinical and Experimental Research, 14(5):756–760, 1990. (109287)

51. Maisto, S.A.; Wolfe, W.; Jordan, J. Short-term motivational therapy. In: P.J. Ott, R.E. Tarter, and R.T. Ammerman, Eds., Sourcebook on Substance Abuse: Etiology, Epidemiology, Assessment, and Treatment, Boston, MA: Allyn and Bacon, 1999. 472 p. (pp. 284–292) (149143)

52. Malik, R.; Washton, A.M.; Stone-Washton, N. Structured outpatient treatment. In: A.M. Washton, Ed., Psychotherapy and Substance Abuse: A Practitioner's Handbook, New York, NY: Guilford Press, 1995. 500 p (pp. 285–294) (129018)

53. Midanik, L.T.; Harford, T.C. Alcohol consumption measurement: Introduction to the workshop. Addiction, 89(4):393–394, 1994. (122931)

54. Mayer, J.E.; Koeningsmark, C.P.S. Self efficacy, relapse and the possibility of posttreatment denial as a stage in alcoholism. Alcoholism Treatment Quarterly, 8(4):1–17, 1992. (114947)

55. McMahon, J.; Jones, B.T. Change process in alcoholics: Client motivation and denial in the treatment of alcoholism within the context of contemporary nursing. Journal of Advanced Nursing, 17(2):173–186, 1992. (114629)

56. Metzger-L. From denial to recovery: Counseling problem drinkers, alcoholics, and their families. San Francisco, CA: Jossey-Bass Publishers, 1988. 326 p. (104417)

57. Midanik-L-T. Perceptual variables as factors in drop-out for alcoholism treatment. 11th Annual Medical-Scientific Conference of NCA, Seattle, WA: May, 1980. 20 p. (049915)

58. Midanik L.T. Client's Perception of Problem Severity and Client/Counselor Agreement of Problem Severity as Factors in Early Dropout from Alcoholism Treatment (Abstract). Alcoholism: Clinical and Experimental Research, 4: 223, 1980. (055287)

59. Miller, W.R. Enhancing motivation for change. In: W.R. Miller and N. Heather, Eds., Treating Addictive Behaviors: Second Edition, New York, NY: Plenum Press, 1998. 357 p. (pp. 121–132) (147748)

60. Miller, W.R. Motivational interviewing: III. On the ethics of motivational intervention. Behavioural and Cognitive Psychotherapy, 22(2):111–123, 1994. (124916)

61. Miller W.R. Increasing motivation for change. In: R.K. Hester and W.R. Miller, Eds., Handbook of Alcoholism Treatment Approaches, Elmsford, NY: Pergamon Press, 1989. 292 p. (pp. 67–80). (103643)

62. MilleR F; Barasch A. Under-reporting of alcohol use: The role of organic mental syndromes. Drug and Alcohol Dependence, 15(4):347–351, 1985. (085793)

63. Morgan, T.J. Behavioral treatment techniques for psychoactive substance use disorders. In: F. Rotgers, D.S. Keller, and J. Morgenstern, Treating Substance Abuse: Theory and Technique, New York, NY: Guilford Press, 1996. 328 p (pp. 202–240) (132594)

64. Morgenstern, J.; Frey, R.M.; McCrady, B.S.; Labouvie, E.; Neighbors, C.J. Examining mediators of change in traditional chemical dependency treatment. Journal of Studies on Alcohol, 57(1):53–64, 1996. (131228)

65. Mulder, R.T.; Joyce, P.R.; Sellman, J.D.; Sullivan, P.F.;

Cloninger, C.R. Towards an understanding of defense style in terms of temperament and character. Acta Psychiatrica Scandinavica, 93(2):99–104, 1996. (142271)

66. Newsome, D.; Ditzler, T. Assessing alcoholic denial: Further examination of the denial rating scale. Journal of Nervous and Mental Disease, 181(11):689–694, 1993. (120930)

67. Obert, J.L.; Rawson, R.A.; Miotto, K. Substance abuse treatment for "hazardous users": An early intervention. Journal of Psychoactive Drugs, 29(3):291–298, 1997. (139788)

68. Oleary Michael R; Rohsenow-Damaris J; Schau-Edward-J. Defensive Style And Treatment Outcome Among Men Alcoholics. Journal of Studies On Alcohol, 38(5):1036–1040, 1977. (029325)

69. Owen-P-L. Measurement of the concept of denial among alcoholics. Dissertation Abstracts International, 45(8):2698–B, 1985. (084176)

70. Paredes-Alfonso. Denial, Deceptive Maneuvers, and Consistency in the Behavior of Alcoholics. in: F. Seixas and R. Cadoret, EDS, The Person with Alcoholism, New York: Academy of Sciences, 1974. 177 p. (pp. 23–33). (015598)

71. Pursch-J-A. Lab test for denial. Alcoholism The National Magazine, 5(4):11, 1985. (077558)

72. Rabold, D.E. Differentiating between psychogenic and neurogenic denial in persons with TBI and substance abuse. Dissertation Abstracts International, 57(7): 4771–B, 1997. (136925)

73. Rebelo, F.R. Denial level and coping style in a substance abuse treatment population. Dissertation Abstracts International, 60(6):2958–B, 1999. (152185)

74. Rhoads-G-A. Preferred psychotherapist style of highly denying alcoholics: An Ericksonian hypnotherapy model. Dissertation Abstracts International, 48(7):2107–B, 1988. (100854)

75. Richardson, D.R. Effects of a videotaped family intervention on the denial level of alcoholics and cocaine abusers. Dissertation Abstracts International, 53(11):3806A, 1993. (119030)

76. Ritson, E.B. III. Alcohol, drugs, and stigma. Interna-

tional Journal of Clinical Practice, 53(7):549–551, 1999. (153504)

77. Rollnick-S. Value of a cognitive-behavioural approach to the treatment of problem drinkers. In: N. Heather, I. Robertson, and P. Davies, Eds., Misuse of Alcohol: Crucial Issues in Dependence Treatment & Prevention, New York, NY: New York University Press, 1985. 284 p. (pp. 135–147). (087987)

78. Rothschild, D. Working with addicts in private practice: Overcoming initial resistance. In: A.M. Washton, Ed., Psychotherapy and Substance Abuse: A Practitioner's Handbook, New York, NY: Guilford Press, 1995. 500 p. (pp. 192–203) (129013)

79. Rugel, R.P.; Barry, D. Overcoming denial through the group: A test of acceptance theory. Small Group Research, 21(1):45–58, 1990. (108985)

80. Runge, E.G. Intervention: Raising the bottom. Journal of the South Carolina Medical Association, 86(1):19–21, 1990. (107394)

81. Saunders, B.; Wilkinson, C.; Towers, T. Motivation and addictive behaviors: Theoretical perspectives. In: F. Rotgers, D.S. Keller, and J. Morgenstern, Treating Substance Abuse: Theory and Technique, New York, NY: Guilford Press, 1996. 328 p. (pp. 241–265) (132595)

82. Shaffer, H.J. Denial, ambivalence, and the countertransferential hate. In: J.D. Levin and R.H. Weiss, R.H. (Eds.), Dynamics and Treatment of Alcoholism: Essential Papers, Northvale, NJ: Jason Aronson, Inc., 1994. 456 p. (pp. 421–437) (127248)

83. Segal-B. Causes of therapeutic failures in alcoholics. Alcoholism: Clinical and Experimental Research, 5(1):167, 1981. (063464)

84. Shore-J-J. Use of paradox in alcoholism treatment. 1980, 21 p. (045314)

85. Smith, M.B.; Hoffmann, N.G.; Nederhoed, R. Development and reliability of the Recovery Attitude and Treatment Evaluator-Questionnaire I (RAATE-QI) International Journal of the Addictions, 30(2):147–160, 1995. (126759)

86. Smith, M.B.; Hoffman, N.G.; Nederhoed, R. Develop-

ment and reliability of RAATE-CE. Journal of Substance Abuse, 4(4):355–363, 1992. (118181)

87. Sjoberg, L. Risk perception of alcohol consumption. Alcoholism: Clinical and Experimental Research, 22(7 suppl.):277S–284S, 1998. (145635)

88. Trice-H-M; Sonnenstuhl-W-J. Constructive confrontation and other referral processes. In: M. Galanter, Ed., Recent Developments in Alcoholism, New York, NY: Plenum Press, 1988. 411 p. (pp. 159–170). (100821)

89. Twerski Abraham. Alcologia: A "Logical" Paralogia. American Journal of Psychoanalysis, 34:257–261, 1974. (020825)

90. Vabret, F.; Cognard, C.; Davy, A. L'arret de l'alcool: difficile separation (Stopping alcohol: A difficult separation) Alcoologie, 20(4):329–333, 1998. (146746)

Wallace-J. Critical issues in alcoholism therapy. In: Sheldon Zimberg, John Wallace, and Sheila Blume (Eds.), Practical Approaches to Alcoholism Psychotherapy. Second Edition, New York, NY: Plenum Press, 1985. 406 p. (pp. 37–49). (079089)

91. Ward, L.C.; Rothaus, P. Measurement of denial and rationalization in male alcoholics. Journal of Clinical Psychology, 47(3):465–468, 1991. (111325)

92. Watten, R.G. Coping styles in abstainers from alcohol. Psychopathology, 29(6):340–346, 1996. (136582)

93. Weinberg Jon R. Why Do Alcoholics Deny Their Problem? Minnesota Medicine, 56(8):709–711, 1973. (009833)

94. Weinstein, B.A.; Raber, M.J.; Slaght, E.F. Reexamining the clinical response to denial in alcoholics. Employee Assistance Quarterly, 14(4):45–52, 1999. (150664)

95. Williams, S.A. Therapeutic factors affecting denial change in substance abuse treatment groups. Dissertation Abstracts International, 57(4):2892–B, 1996. (135500)

96. Wing, D.M. Transcending alcoholic denial. Image: Journal of Nursing Scholarship, 27(2):121–126, 1995. (144468)

97. Wing, D.M.; Hammer-Higgins, P. Determinants of denial: A study of alcoholics. Journal of Psychosocial Nursing and Mental Health Services, 31(2):13–17, 1993. (136784)

98. Wiseman, E.J.; Souder, E.; O'Sullivan, P. Relation of denial of alcohol problems to neurocognitive impairment and depression. Psychiatric Services, 47(3):306–308, 1996. (132111)

99. Zimberg-S. Individual therapy. Clinical Management of Alcoholism, New York, NY: Brunner/Mazel, 1982. 251 p. (pp. 70–80). (067156)

100. Wallace J. Critical Issues in Alcoholism Therapy. In: Practical Approaches to Alcoholism Psychotherapy, New York: Plenum, 1978, Vol. XIX. 288 p. (pp. 31–43). (039526)

101. Wallace J. Working with the Preferred Defense Structure of the Recovering Alcoholic. In: Practical Approaches to Alcoholism Psychotherapy, New York: Plenum, 1978, Vol. XIX. 288 p. (pp.19–29). (039525)

102. Zimberg-S. Principles of alcoholism psychotherapy. In: Sheldon Zimberg, John Wallace, and Sheila Blume (Eds.), Practical Approaches to Alcoholism Psychotherapy. Second Edition, New York, NY: Plenum Press, 1985. 406 p. (pp. 3–22). (079087)

103. Zimberg-S. Office psychotherapy of alcoholism. In: J. Solomon, Ed., Alcoholism and Clinical Psychiatry, New York, NY: Plenum Medical Book, 1982. 238 p. (pp. 213-229). (070241)

104. Zweben-J-E. Recovery-oriented psychotherapy: Patient resistances and therapist dilemmas. Journal of Substance Abuse Treatment, 6(2):123–132, 1989. (103469)

105. Zimberg-S. Principles of Alcoholism Psychotherapy. In: Practical Approaches to Alcoholism Psychotherapy, New York: Plenum, 1978, Vol. XIX. 288 p. (pp. 3-18). (039524)

106. Zung B.J. Factor Structure of the Michigan Alcoholism Screening Test. J. STUD. ALC., 39: 56–67, 1978. (033569)

Appendix #1

Denial Self-Monitoring Form

The following checklist was developed by Terence T. Gorski and the CENAPS® Team to help you learn about and identify your denial patterns. You can visit *www.relapse.org* or *www.cenaps.com* for more information.

Part 1: What denial patterns did you use during this part of the exercise? Check as many as needed.

❑ 1. Avoidance: "I'll talk about anything but my real problems!"

❑ 2. Absolute Denial: "No, not me, I don't have problems!"

❑ 3. Minimizing: "My problems aren't that bad!"

❑ 4. Rationalizing: "If I can find good enough reasons for my problems, I won't have to deal with them!"

❑ 5. Blaming: "If I can prove that my problems are not my fault, I won't have to deal with them!"

❑ 6. Comparing: "Showing that others are worse than me proves that I don't have serious problems!"

❑ 7. Compliance: "I'll pretend to do what you want if you'll leave me alone!"

❑ 8. Manipulating: "I'll only admit that I have problems if you agree to solve them for me"

❑ 9. Flight into Health: "Feeling better means that I'm cured!"

❑ 10. Recovery by Fear: "Being scared of my problems will make them go away!"

❑ 11. Strategic Hopelessness: "Since nothing works, I don't have to try!"

❑ 12. Democratic Disease State: "I have the right to destroy myself and no one has the right to stop me!"

Part 2: When did you notice you were using denial?

A. Not until after completing this part of the exercise and reading my answers.

B. While I was answering the questions.

C. I noticed the urge to start using denial before I started to answer the question, but I ended up using denial when I answered the questions anyway.

D. I noticed the urge to start using denial before I started to answer the question, so I stopped my denial and answered the questions honestly.

Appendix #2

Denial Management Checklist

The following checklist was developed by Terence T. Gorski and the CENAPS® Team to help you learn about and identify your denial patterns. You can visit *www.relapse.org* or *www.cenaps.com* for more information.

❑ 1. Avoidance: "I'll talk about anything but my real problems!"

❑ 2. Absolute Denial: "No, not me, I don't have problems!"

❑ 3. Minimizing: "My problems aren't that bad!"

❑ 4. Rationalizing: "If I can find good enough reasons for my problems, I won't have to deal with them!"

❑ 5. Blaming: "If I can prove that my problems are not my fault, I won't have to deal with them!"

❑ 6. Comparing: "Showing that others are worse than me proves that I don't have serious problems!"

❑ 7. Compliance: "I'll pretend to do what you want if you'll leave me alone!"

❑ 8. Manipulating: "I'll only admit that I have problems if you agree to solve them for me"

❑ 9. Flight into Health: "Feeling better means that I'm cured!"

❑ 10. Recovery by Fear: "Being scared of my problems will make them go away!"

❑ 11. Strategic Hopelessness: "Since nothing works, I don't have to try!"

❑ 12. Democratic Disease State: "I have the right to destroy myself and no one has the right to stop me!"

Appendix #3

Samples of Personalized Denial Patterns

The following samples of personalized denial patterns were developed by Terence T. Gorski and the CENAPS® Team to help you personalize the denial patterns you selected. You can visit *www.relapse.org* or *www.cenaps.com* for more information.

1. (Avoidance) **Skating off the Walls:** I know I'm using denial when I refuse to directly answer a question and keep trying to change the subject.

2. (Absolute Denial) **Saying It Isn't So:** I know I'm using denial when I tell people that I don't have a problem even though I know deep inside that I do.

3. (Minimizing) **Saying It Isn't That Bad:** I know I'm using denial when I admit I have a problem, but try to tell people that it isn't as bad as they think it is.

4. (Rationalizing) **Giving Good Reasons:** I know I'm using denial when I try to convince people that there are good reasons for me to have the problem and that because there are good reasons I shouldn't be responsible for having to deal with it.

5. (Blaming) **Saying It's Not My Fault:** I know I'm using denial when I try to blame someone else for my problem and deny that I am responsible for dealing with it.

6. (Comparison) **Criticizing Others:** I know I'm using denial when I point out how bad other people's problems are and use that as a reason why my problems aren't so bad.

7. (Compliance) **Being a Good Little Boy:** I know I'm using denial when I start telling people what they want to hear to get them off my back.

8. (Manipulating) **Getting Over On Others:** I know I'm using denial when I try to get other people to handle the problems for me.

9. (Flight into Health) **Suddenly Cured:** I know I'm using denial when I believe that my problems have suddenly gone away without my doing anything to solve them.

10. (Recovery by Fear) **Scared Straight:** I know I'm using denial when I tell myself that I could never use alcohol or drugs again because I'm so afraid of what will happen if I start drinking and drugging.

11. (Strategic Hopelessness) **Why Bother?:** I know I'm using denial when I tell myself that I can never solve my problems and that other people should just leave me alone.

12. (Democratic Disease State) **I Have My Rights:** I know I'm using denial when I tell other people that I have a right to use alcohol and drugs regardless of what happens and that they have no right to try to stop me.

Appendix #4

Presenting Problem Worksheet

The following checklist was developed by Terence T. Gorski and the CENAPS® Team to help you learn about and identify your denial patterns. You can visit *www.relapse.org* or *www.cenaps.com* for more information.

1. Presenting Problems:	2. Relationship to Alcohol or Drug Use:	3. Consequences of Continued Use:
What are the presenting problems that caused you to seek treatment at this time?	How is each presenting problem related to your use of alcohol or drugs?	What will happen to your ability to solve this problem if you don't stop using alcohol and drugs?
Problem #1:		Best:
		Worst:
		Most likely:
Problem #1:		Best:
		Worst:
		Most likely:
Problem #1:		Best:
		Worst:
		Most likely:

Appendix #5:

The Feeling Management Skills Checklist:

Another tool called **The Feeling Management Skills Checklist** identifies fourteen basic skills for managing feelings and emotions. Remember, many people use denial because they feel overwhelmed by intense unmanageable feelings. By teaching clients to recognize, label, and express feelings in a self environment they can feel less threatened and their need to use rigidly held denial patterns as a survival tool will decrease.

Instructions: Read each of the following statements and rate how true it is on a scale of 0–10. (0 means the statement is not at all true and 10 means the statement is totally true).

❑ 1. I anticipate situations that cause strong feelings and emotions.

❑ 2. I recognize when I am starting to have a strong feeling or emotion.

❑ 3. I can stop myself from reacting to the feeling without thinking it through.

❑ 4. I am able to call a time-out in emotionally-charged situations before my feelings become unmanageable.

❑ 5. I am able to use an immediate relaxation technique to bring down the intensity of the feeling.

❑ 6. I can take a deep breath and notice what I'm feeling.

❑ 7. I can find words that describe what I'm feeling and use the feeling list when necessary.

❑ 8. I can rate the intensity of my feelings using a ten-point scale.

❑ 9. I can consciously acknowledge the feeling and how strong it is by saying to myself, "Right now I'm feeling _____ and it's OK to be feeling this way."

❏ 10. I can identify the thoughts that make me feel this way. I can ask myself, "How can I change my thinking in a way that will make me feel better?"

❏ 11. I can identify what I'm doing that's making me feel this way. I can ask myself, "How can I change what I'm doing in a way that will make me feel better?"

❏ 12. I can recognize and resist urges to create problems, hurt myself, or hurt other people.

❏ 13. I can recognize my resistance to doing things that would help me or my situation, and I force myself to do those things despite the resistance.

❏ 14. I can get outside of myself and recognize and respond to what other people are feeling.

Appendix #6

The Feeling Identification CheckList

The Feeling Identification Checklist consists of eight pairs of feeling words. Each pair of feeling words represents feelings that are opposites such as happy or sad, strong or weak, etc. Clients are asked to select the word that best matches what they are feeling, to rate how intense the feeling is on a scale of 0–10 (0 being least intense and 10 being most intense), and why they rated the feeling that way. This last question normally surfaces the self-talk that is activating or intensifying the feeling.

The Feeling Identification Checklist		
Are you feeling	How intense is the feeling? (0–10)	Why do you rate it that way?
❑ 1. **Strong** or **Weak?**		
❑ 2. **Caring** or **Angry?**		
❑ 3. **Happy** or **Sad?**		
❑ 4. **Safe** or **Threatened?**		
❑ 5. **Fulfilled** or **Frustrated?**		
❑ 6. **Proud** or **Ashamed?**		
❑ 7. **Connected** or **Lonely?**		
❑ 8. **Peaceful** or **Agitated?**		

Contact Information

GORSKI-CENAPS® is a training and consultation organization committed to providing the most effective clinical skills training available. Managing denial and resistance is one of many clinical skills training courses that are available. For more information you can call us at 708-799-5000, Fax us at 708-799-5032, or e-mail us at *info@cenaps.com.* Our Web site is *www.cenaps.com* and contains a clinical bulletin board for posting questions or reporting on progress or problems with various aspects of the GORSKI-CENAPS® Model.

Denial Management Counseling Workboo

Practical Exercises for Motivating Substance Abusers to Recover

By Terence T. Gorski
With Stephen F. Grinstead

Learn to Effectively Manage Denial
In the Treatment of Addiction and Related Personali
and Mental Disorders

The Denial Management Workbook is designed to help people overcor
denial, recognize their addiction, and make a personal commitment to recc
ery.

Denial is a normal and natural response for coping with painful and overwhelr
ing problems. This workbook describes the twelve most common denial patter
and guides the reader through a series of exercises that help them to identify ar
more effectively manage their own denial.

The structured exercises contained in this workbook teach the reader ho
to recognize and more effectively manage their denial when it occurs. Oth
exercises invite the client to put these new skills to use by identifying and cla
fying the problems that caused them to seek help, their life and addiction hi
tory, and their personal symptoms of addiction. Clients are then guided throuc
the process of making a firm and deep commitment to taking a next step
recovery.

ISBN 0-8309-08501

The Denial Management Counseling Workbook *Practical Exercises for Motivating Substance Abusers to Recover*	
Exercise #1: Understanding Denial As a Part of the Human Condition	**Exercise #5:** Stopping Denial As You Think About Your Problems
Exercise #2: Understanding the Principles of Denial Management	**Exercise #6:** Stopping Denial As You Think About Your Life History
Exercise #3: Recognizing Your Denial	**Exercise #7:** Stopping Denial As You Think About Your Addiction
Exercise #4: Managing Your Denial	
	Exercise #8: Stopping Denial As You Decide What To Do Next
	Exercise #9: Evaluating Your Denial Management Skills